RADAR
LICENSE
ENDORSEMENT
HANDBOOK

by Edward M. Noll

HOWARD W. SAMS & CO., INC.
THE BOBBS-MERRILL CO., INC.
INDIANAPOLIS · KANSAS CITY · NEW YORK

FIRST EDITION

THIRD PRINTING—1969

Preface

In the last decade there has been a tremendous upsurge in the use of marine radar. The biggest contributing factor to this rise has been the increase in small-boat traffic, both private and commercial.

In order to service marine radar, the holder of a first- or second-class radiotelephone or radiotelegraph license must obtain a radar endorsement. Such an endorsement is required specifically for working on marine radar. Although a first- or second-class license is required for servicing aircraft, industrial, weather, and other forms of radar, the special endorsement is not a prerequisite.

This handbook is designed to prepare you for the FCC Element 8 examination, which deals with marine radar. It does not solely serve as a question and answer guide; it also covers radar fundamentals, plus practical information about modern marine and other radar equipment.

Your responsibilities after a radar endorsement is obtained are also considered. The included tables, laws, and procedures will continue to serve as invaluable aids long after you have passed the examination.

EDWARD M. NOLL

Dedicated to
GREGORY E. NOLL
Walk in wonder, young man.
You will listen through windows in the heavens,
And Canopus shall be a sign.

Contents

CHAPTER 1

Principles

In less than a decade *small boating* has become a major business. Waterways on occasion appear clogged with traffic. Add to this the steady growth in commercial off-shore boating and inland water traffic and you can well understand the rising concern with safe navigation practices and devices. One such safety device is radar. Regardless of atmospheric conditions, it can be used with precision to detect buoys, boats, shore lines, and other obstacles. Although there have been collisions between radar-equipped vessels, investigations usually prove that radar screens were ignored or improperly read.

Radar is used principally for harbor, shore-line, and inland-waterways traffic. The larger ocean-going vessels can also make use of higher-powered and longer-range radar when traveling in mid-ocean during darkness and inclement weather.

Certainly modern radar is not limited to marine applications. Small radars are available for planes. Large commercial aircraft use radar for avoiding thunderheads and bad weather areas, as well as obstacle avoidance and traffice monitoring. Giant land-based radars monitor the airways continuously, following traffic in and out of airdromes and along the civil airways. Add to this the vast array of military radar installations and you can understand that radar has become a prime warning and navigational instrument.

1-1. RADIO ECHOES

Radar is fundamentally a distance-measuring system using the principle of radio-echoing. All of you have heard an echo of your own voice as it has been bounced off a cliff or a distant large-area reflecting surface. Equipped with an accurate timing device plus a knowledge of the speed at which sound travels, you can determine just how many hundreds of yards away the point of sound reflection is located. You have heard that bats in their nocturnal and cave travels use supersonic sounds for obstacle avoidance and for locating swarms of insects. The porpoise uses similar audio soundings in his underwater travel.

A radio wave travels many times faster than a sound wave. Nevertheless, with suitable instrumentation radar can be used to measure the distance, or range, to a surface that reflects radio waves. In fact, the word radar is a contraction of its definition— RAdio Detection And Ranging.

Radio waves travel at the speed of 300 million meters per second, or approximately 186 thousand miles per second. These figures can be brought down accurately to any number of practical rule-of-thumb distance constants. The most common of these constants are given in Table 1-1.

It must be stressed that radar ranging is a two-way process. As shown in Fig. 1-1, the radio wave must travel out and back,

Table 1-1. Radar Wave Propagation

186,000	Miles Per Second
162,000	Nautical Miles Per Second
3×10^8	Meters Per Second
3.28×10^8	Yards Per Second
0.186	Statute Miles Per Microsecond
0.162	Nautical Miles Per Microsecond
328	Yards Per Microsecond

Radar Timing

10.75	Microseconds Per Mile
12.36	Microseconds Per Nautical Mile
164	Yards Per Microsecond
0.081	Nautical Miles Per Microsecond

and therefore the distance that the wave travels is twice the distance between the radar and the reflecting obstacle. In terms of nautical measurement, a radio wave travels 162,000 nautical miles per second. This corresponds to 0.162 nautical mile per microsecond (one microsecond equals one millionth of a second).

Because the radio wave must travel out and back, the actual radar-range velocity is usually stated as 0.081 nautical mile per microsecond. In other words, an obstacle 0.081 nautical mile away from the radar would require a total radar wave travel time of one microsecond (one-half microsecond out and one-half microsecond back).

Since a nautical mile is equal to 2,027 yards, the velocity of radio-wave travel is equivalent to 328 yards per microsecond. However, effective radar velocity for range measurement purposes is again one-half of this true radio-wave velocity; it is 164 yards per microsecond.

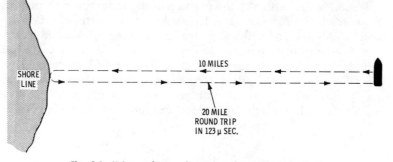

Fig. 1-1. Using radar to determine the distance to land.

In the example of Fig. 1-1 the distance to the shore line is to be determined. The radar instrumentation indicates that the radar wave in traveling out and back requires an elapsed time of 123.44 microseconds. This indicates that the range to the nearest land is 10 nautical miles (0.081×123.44).

In using a radar set it is not necessary to clock how many microseconds it takes the radio wave to travel out and back, or to make any sort of calculation using radar range velocity and elapsed time. The radar set as such is calibrated in terms of range, yards, and/or knots. The radar display directly indicates the distance to a reflecting surface.

The radar display may indicate the typical ranges shown in Fig. 1-2. If it is indicating that your position is 1000 yards to the left bank and 800 yards to the right bank, the actual radar signals are making round-trip excursions in 6.1 (1000/164) and 4.88 (800/164) microseconds respectively. Up ahead there is another vessel some 500 yards on the left, and 2000 yards ahead is a pair of buoys. These correspond to elapsed times of 3.05 and 12.2 microseconds respectively.

The display of information, as shown in Fig. 1-2, is quite similar to what you would see on the most common type of radar display. However, the background would be black and the actual targets would be illuminated. In addition, there would be several concentric illuminated rings which are called range rings or markings. They calibrate the display in terms of distance from the radar set. In the example, calibrations are in terms of thousands of yards.

1-2. BEARING

A radar set is not only able to determine the range to a point of reflection, but it also determines the bearing of the point of reflection with relation to the position of the radar, or with respect to some other reference direction such as true north, etc. For the usual shipboard radar the ship heading is often established as the zero degree reference angle, as depicted in Fig. 1-2.

Radar signals are transmitted on an extremely high frequency. Therefore the wavelength is very short, and it is possible to build highly directional antennas with practical dimensions. Microwave signals travel in straight light-beam fashion. These characteristics

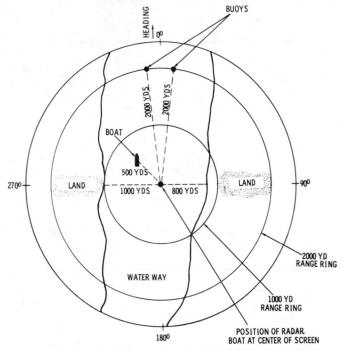

Fig. 1-2. Typical inland water conditions as evaluated by radar.

make it possible to concentrate the radar energy into a small-diameter, pencil-like beam. Thus, the direction from which a reflection returns to the radar set is indicated by the angular position of the radar antenna at that instant. This fact is illustrated in Fig. 1-3. If the antenna is pointing directly north there will be a reflection from obstacle 1. Since the reflection occurs when the antenna is pointing in the direction of the ship's heading, it is indicated that the obstacle is at zero degrees, or dead ahead. Likewise, with the antenna directed at an angle 30° or 135° relative to the ship's heading, there will be a return echo indicating that there are obstacles in these directions. At other angles in the example of Fig. 1-3, there will be no return echo signals.

In summary, a radar is able to determine the range to an obstacle or target by evaluating the time needed for a signal to go out to the target and return. The bearing of the target is shown by the angle of the antenna when the target signal returns. These two factors are of particular importance in using radar for marine navigation and safety.

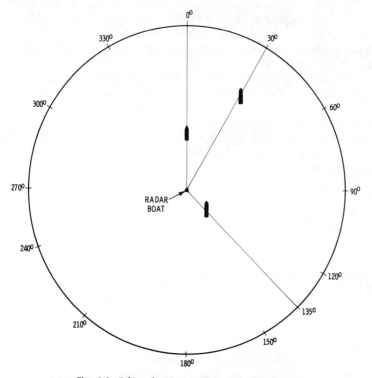

Fig. 1-3. Taking bearings with a radar display.

1-3. TARGET MAKE UP

Radar can be used to evaluate additional attributes of a target that is returning echoes to the set. The size of the image as it appears on the radar display tube gives some inkling of the dimensions of the target. A large vessel produces a larger mark or "blip" than a smaller vessel produces; a buoy appears smaller than a vessel. The shore line illuminates a much larger segment of the display, indicating a large land mass. A large island illuminates a larger area on the radar display tube than does a smaller island.

The greater the range to a target of a given size the smaller is its corresponding blip on the display screen. A stationary target appears stationary on the display. The faster the target moves, the faster it moves across the display tube as compared to a slower moving target. There are radar systems that can accurately determine the actual velocity and direction of motion of a moving target.

The strength of a return signal from a given range can also give a clue to the make up of the target. A metallic surface reflects a strong signal. A large target made of wood or other material that does not reflect radio waves well returns a much weaker echo, or no echo signal at all.

The ability to "read" a radar display separates the good radar operator from the mediocre one. Interpretive skill comes with practice. Practice when vision is good so that you can "see" the object and its corresponding blip.

To summarize again, radar can be used to determine target range, target bearing, and something about the physical attributes and motion of the target.

1-4. ELEVATION ANGLE

Radar can also be used to determine the height of a target. Just as the azimuth angle in which the antenna is pointed determines the bearing of a target, the elevation of the antenna provides a second angle that can be used to determine the height of a target. Hence it is possible for a land-based radar, as in Fig. 1-4, to determine the range, bearing, and height of an aircraft target. With suitable facilities the same radar can be used to determine the velocity and direction of flight of the aircraft under observation.

Furthermore, an elaborate radar system of this type is able to "lock" on such a target, and the antenna system automatically follows the flight path of the target. This is referred to as *"target acquisition."* The same techniques, in very elaborate form, can be used to "track" satellites, such as Telstar, and other types of space vehicles.

A radar installation in an aircraft can be used to determine the range, bearing, and elevation of other aircraft in the vicinity. In a similar manner an aircraft-installed radar is able to follow thunderheads and other storms, locating their exact position and making the necessary bearing and altitude corrections to avoid contact.

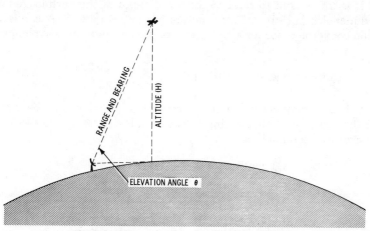

Fig. 1-4. Using radar for elevation measurements.

In the example of Fig. 1-4 the elevation angle and range are known quantities. By making suitable corrections for the curvature of the earth, the exact height of the target can be determined. An approximation of the target height can be determined using simple trigonometry as shown:

$$\text{height} = \text{range} \times \sin \theta$$

1-5. RADAR FREQUENCIES

Radar sets operate at extremely high frequencies because of the light-like characteristics and ease with which microwaves can be concentrated into a small-diameter beam. The specific assignments made for shipboard radar operation are given in Table 1-2. These are in the S and X band spectra.

That the frequency of operation is high can be emphasized when we consider that the AM broadcast band is centered about a frequency of only 1 mc. Thus the average radar set operates on a frequency that is several thousand times higher than that of a radio broadcast signal.

Table 1-2. Commercial Ship Radar Frequencies

Frequency (mc)	Band	Wavelength (cm)
2900-3100	S	10.3 -9.7
5470-5650	X	5.5 -5.3
9300-9500	X	3.22-3.15

It is convenient to refer to the wavelength of the various radar frequencies in terms of centimeters instead of meters. A convenient conversion formula between frequency and cm wavelength is:

$$\text{centimeter wavelength (cm)} = \frac{30,000}{\text{frequency in megacycles}}$$

It is also convenient to relate centimeters and inches because of the practical dimensioning of waveguides, antennas, and other microwave components.

$$1 \text{ centimeter} = 0.394 \text{ inches}$$
$$1 \text{ inch} = 2.54 \text{ centimeters}$$

1-6. BEARING RESOLUTION AND BEAM DIMENSIONS

In previous paragraphs we considered the range angle (azimuth angle) and elevation angle of a radiated radar signal. Two other angles of concern, as shown in Fig. 1-5, involve the horizontal and vertical beam dimensions. It is customary to measure beam angles between the half-power points; these points correspond to the angles set off by the 3-db down points (points at which the signal voltage is down 29.3% and signal power is down 50%). Some radar beams are symmetrical; that is, the horizontal and vertical angles are the same, and therefore the beam has a circular cross section. Beam angles vary between a small fractional part of a degree and tens of degrees, depending on the

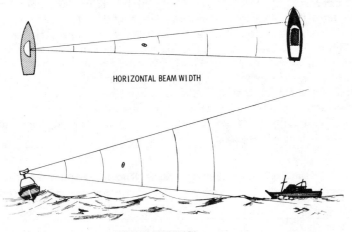

HORIZONTAL BEAM WIDTH

VERTICAL BEAM WIDTH

Fig. 1-5. Antenna beam widths.

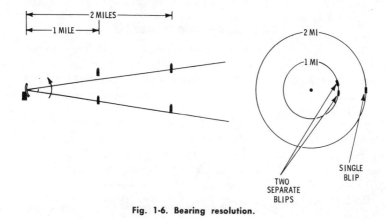

Fig. 1-6. Bearing resolution.

radar service that is to be rendered. Beam angles are dependent on antenna type and dimensions.

Most small-boat and ship radar antennas have a narrow horizontal angle and a substantially broader vertical angle. Thus the cross section of the beam is approximately rectangular.

Bearing resolution has to do with the capability of a radar system to delineate between two obstacles that are the same distance away but of a different bearing. It represents the ability of a radar to display two separate blips when two targets are very near each other. Technically it is the minimum bearing difference between two targets which will be reproduced as separate images on the radar display. If the minimum bearing difference that will reproduce as two images is 3 degrees, the bearing resolution at two miles is greater than it is for a 1-mile range.

Bearing resolution is illustrated in Fig. 1-6. It is to be noted that the minimum *separation* between two targets that can be so displayed increases with range. For example, the minimum separation at two miles is greater than it is for a 1 mile range.

A number of factors can influence the bearing resolution. A principal consideration is the beam dimension. In terms of shipboard application, it is the horizontal angle or beam width which has the major influence on the bearing resolution. The more the beam can be concentrated horizontally, the better the bearing resolution.

For those applications where the elevation or vertical angle is also of significance, the vertical beam width also influences the resolution of the radar system. For example, in distinguishing two aircraft targets it is equally important to know whether the one aircraft is above or below the other. Therefore, bearing resolution and elevation resolution are both significant.

15

1-7. MICROWAVE PULSES

There are various forms of radar transmission. The most common type of transmission is called pulse radar. Pulse radar sets are widely installed on small boats and ocean-going vessels. A high-powered radar transmitter sends out a pulse of microwave energy. The transmitter then shuts down, and the radar receiver listens for returning echoes from this burst of microwave energy. Radar pulses vary in duration from less than one microsecond up to five or more microseconds. Depending on the type of radar service to be rendered, from sixty pulses up to several thousand pulses are sent out per second.

Under all circumstances the *transmit time* is substantially shorter than the *receive time*. This is a necessity, because the receiver must listen for an elapsed time equal to the time of travel out to a target at maximum range, and back again to the receiver. Recall that a radar nautical mile corresponds to an excursion time of 12.3 microseconds. If the maximum range of a particular radar set is 40 miles, the total elapsed time will be 492 microseconds (40 × 12.3). Thus the receiver must listen for at least this minimum elapsed time before the next pulse can be sent out, as shown in Fig. 1-7.

In the illustration it has been assumed that the duration of the pulse is 2 microseconds. The time spacing between the end of one pulse and the beginning of the next pulse has been assigned a value of 498 microseconds. Thus, the radar pulse will have adequate time to travel 40 miles and return. Of course, the receive time is more than adequate for any target that is nearer to the radar set.

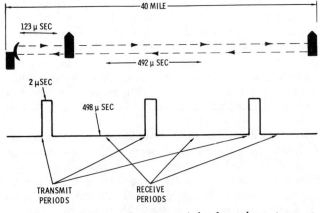

Fig. 1-7. Transmit and receive periods of a radar system.

If the conditions just mentioned apply to a maximum 40-mile range, what is the maximum number of 2-microsecond pulses that can be transmitted per second? The time interval between the start of one pulse and the start of the next corresponds to 500 microseconds. This is the pulse period. The transmission frequency can be determined by dividing the pulse period into one million microseconds (1 second).

$$\text{frequency or PRR} = \frac{1 \text{ second}}{\text{period}} = \frac{10^6 \text{ microseconds}}{500} = 2000$$

The number of pulses that can be transmitted per second is 2000, and the pulse-repetition-rate (PRR) or pulses-per-second (PPS) is said to be 2000.

Of course, a greater range of transmission requires a longer listening period. Consequently, fewer pulses may be transmitted per second. For a shorter range, the pulse repetition rate can be even higher, because the listening period can be correspondingly less.

Fig. 1-7 shows the timing of a radar signal which has traveled out to a target 40 miles away and returned over the same path to the radar set. A second target is also shown on the illustration. It returns a signal from a distance of approximately 10 miles. Notice that its echo comes back much earlier than the previous echo signal. Its excursion trip time is only 123 microseconds.

Some radar sets have ranges in excess of several hundred miles. Under these conditions the pulse-repetition rate must be quite low because of the long receive period required.

1-8. PULSE POWER AND DUTY CYCLE

It is apparent from the previous discussion that the radar transmitter functions for only a small portion of each second. During these intervals of transmission a high peak power is radiated. However, if the power is averaged over an entire second, it is found to be very much lower. Consequently, radar transmitters have a high peak-power output but a low average-power output. Peak-power outputs vary from one thousand watts up to millions of peak watts. The usual shipboard radar sets have peak-power outputs that range from 3 kw up to several hundreds of kilowatts.

The average power output of a radar transmitter can be calculated in a simple manner. One need only determine for what fraction of a second radar power is being transmitted. In the example of Fig. 1-7 the pulse duration was 2 microseconds and 2000 of these pulses were transmitted each second. Consequently the transmit time per second is:

$$\text{Transmit Time} = 2\ \mu\ \text{sec} \times 2000 = 4000\ \mu\ \text{sec}$$

The radar transmitter transmits 4000 microseconds out of each one million microseconds. This quotient is referred to as the *duty cycle* of the radar.

$$\text{Duty Cycle} = \frac{\text{Transmit Time}}{10^6} = 0.004$$

Furthermore, if the peak power of the radar is known, the average power can be determined by multiplying the peak value by the duty cycle. Again in the previous example the average power is calculated to be:

$$\text{Average Power} = 0.004 \times \text{Peak Power}$$

The higher the duty cycle, the greater the average power output is. Duty cycle is increased by increasing pulse duration and/or

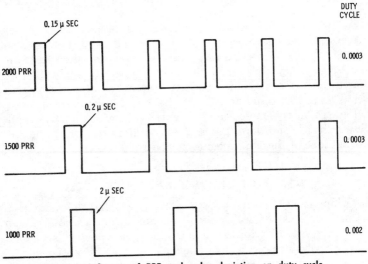

Fig. 1-8. Influence of PRR and pulse deviation on duty cycle.

pulse repetition rate. This is apparent when we consider that when more pulses per second or wider pulses are sent out, the total transmit time will be increased. Several duty-cycle calculations are given in Fig. 1-8. Note that the first two have the same duty cycle; the first using a short pulse with a high repetition rate and the second with a longer pulse but a shorter repetition rate.

In addition to the required listen period several other factors, according to the desired radar service, influence the pulse duration and pulse repetition rate. The average strength of a returning radar signal can be increased by using a long duration pulse. In so doing the duty cycle is high, but the returning echo has a higher average signal strength. However, there are limitations to the increase in pulse duration. For example, for the observation of a short range target it is possible that an echo would return before the transmit pulse is completed.

As disclosed previously, a high repetition rate reduces the listening period. Therefore it is conceivable that a second pulse will be transmitted before the echo returns from the first pulse as reflected from a distant target. Of course, a high duty cycle also means that the average power output and input requirements are increased. This introduces weight, economy, and other equipment factors.

In general, for long range operation the pulse duration is long and the repetition rate low. The long duration pulse means that the average power output is higher and the average level of the return echo is higher. This means a greater range of transmission. At the same time the lower repetition rate increases the pulse period and provides an adequate listening period for the return of a distant echo. For short range operation it is customary to use a very short pulse and a fast repetition rate. The short pulse means that the radar receiver is ready to listen to the return from a nearby target. The fast repetition rate makes sure that the average power level is maintained at an adequate level by sending pulses at a faster rate to the targets.

1-9. FUNCTIONAL BLOCK DIAGRAMS

The functional block diagram of a typical radar installation is given in Fig. 1-9. Study the diagram carefully and understand the basic objective of each major unit. Know this block diagram and those that follow in this chapter so well that you can draw them from memory. This understanding of the fundamental operation of a radar set is important in preparing for your radar license examination.

The major units are shown in the block diagram. The timing center of a radar set is called the *timer*. It generates a basic set of timing pulses that trigger and control the generation of the pulses that turn on the radar *transmitter*. In effect, the timer decides the pulse repetition rate of the radar system.

The transmitter contains the high-powered microwave generator. It is usually a magnetron power oscillator. The responsibility of the magnetron is to generate a high-powered RF pulse of proper duration and repetition rate. The power pulses that turn on the magnetron are generated in the *modulator*. The modulator pulse generator is always under the control of timing pulses from the timer.

The oscillator operates only during the power pulse and sends out a burst of microwave energy through the *duplexer* and *wave guide* to the *antenna*. Then the transmitter shuts down, and the *receiver* listens. The return echoes from a distant target strike the same antenna, and through the wave guide and duplexer, the return signals enter the receiver. Here they are increased in level and demodulated. The signals are next applied to an *indicator* and are observed on a special cathode-ray oscilloscope *display tube*. The scope display and associated circuits are calibrated by the

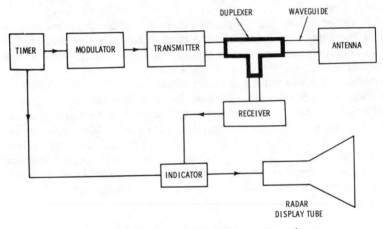

Fig. 1-9. General functional block diagram of a radar set.

timer so that an actual time measurement can be made between the time of pulse transmission and the time of echo arrival. In so doing a conversion is made between time and distance.

The indicator display also takes into consideration the direction to which the antenna is pointed when an echo returns. Consequently the radar display can also be calibrated in terms of bearing.

Two special devices, included in the duplexer (Fig. 1-10), are TR and anti-TR (or ATR) tubes. The TR or transmit-receive tube protects the receiver when the transmitter is in operation. On transmit it places a short circuit across the receiver input. Consequently the high-powered transmit pulse will not injure or delay the operation of the radar receiver. The ATR device permits the receiver to make full use of a weak returning echo signal. It blocks the return signal from the transmitter section

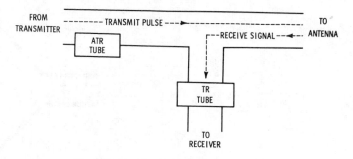

Fig. 1-10. Functional diagram of a duplexer.

and directs the return signals into the receiver with minimum loss.

The receiver is very sensitive, and to maintain the very best signal-to-noise ratio it converts the high-frequency microwave signal to a lower IF frequency before amplification. The signal is then increased in level and demodulated in preparation for its application to the indicator section.

In the indicator section of the radar set there is further signal processing along with the introduction of calibration signals which are formed under control of the timer. Also under the control of the timer, the indicator develops the necessary sweep waveforms used to deflect the beam of the CRT radar display tube.

1-10.   RADAR DISPLAYS

There are several different types of radar displays. For shipboard use the so-called PPI (Plan-Position-Indicator) type of display is used almost exclusively. It is also the most common type of display used in aircraft radar. Before discussing the PPI type of presentation a more simple type of display will be described as an introduction to the subject.

1-10-1.   A-Scope Display

An A-type presentation can be understood readily because of its similarity to the operation of a test oscilloscope. As shown in Fig. 1-11, a sawtooth sweep waveform is applied to the horizontal deflection system. As in a conventional test oscilloscope, this sawtooth wave traces a single horizontal line across the screen of the radar scope. Inasmuch as the sawtooth rise is linear, a linear time base line is established.

The horizontal sweep frequency corresponds to the pulse repetition rate of the radar system. The start of each sweep motion

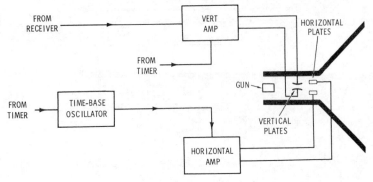

Fig. 1-11. A-scope functional block diagram.

across the screen is synchronized to the transmitted radar pulse by a timing trigger.

The signal information to be observed, as per conventional oscilloscope practice, is applied to the vertical deflection system. Any received signal will cause a vertical deflection of the scanning beam as it makes its left to right trip across the screen. Not only is the returning target signal applied to the vertical deflection system, but a start pulse, which coincides with the transmit-pulses, as well as various range-calibration pulses, is added to the vertical-deflection signal.

The various signals as they are reproduced on the A-scope display are shown in Fig. 1-12. As in a previous example, let us assume that we are operating on a 40-mile range. When the radar pulse is transmitted, a time-coincident pulse is applied to the input of the vertical amplifier of the A-scope type of indicator. As shown in Fig. 1-12 it appears at the extreme left side of the display.

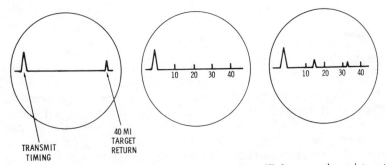

(A) Transmit pulse and 40 mile target. (B) Range marks, no target. (C) Range marks and target signals

Fig. 1-12. A-scope displays.

The horizontal trace of an A-scope moves left to right across the screen. Its timing coincides with the motion of the radar pulse as it travels through space toward a target. In fact, the trace on the A-scope moves from the left extreme to the right extreme in the same time required for the round trip of the radar signal out to a 40-mile target and back. Exactly 492 microseconds after transmission an echo signal from the target enters the receiver, is amplified, and is applied to the vertical deflection system. It causes a vertical deflection of the beam when it is at the far right.

For a practical A-scope display, the screen is more finely calibrated. In fact, special range-mark pulses are generated within the indicator. In Fig. 1-12 you will note that small marks appear at four different spots along the horizontal trace. Actually they calibrate the presentation at 10-mile intervals. The first range-mark signal is generated 123 microseconds after the transmit pulse. This corresponds to a round-trip travel time of 10 miles. Thus its position on the display would be exactly coincident with any echo coming back from a 10-mile target. The second range-calibration pulse is applied to the vertical-deflection system 246 microseconds after the transmit pulse. It places a calibration mark at a point which corresponds to a 20-mile round-trip time. A range calibration system thus places equidistantly spaced range markers along the trace, calibrating the time base line in miles, yards, or some other desired unit of distance.

With the range marks present it is possible to make a rather quick reading of target range. Example C shows the range marks as well as two target signals. One is coming back from a distance of 15 miles; the second echo appears at approximately 32 miles.

The A-scope presentation permits a measure of target range, but it does not show the target bearing. The bearing can be obtained by determining the direction toward which the antenna is directed when there is a maximum received echo from a particular target. The alignment of the antenna on a given target can be done manually or automatically.

The influence of antenna orientation is shown in Fig. 1-13. When the antenna is directed "on target," there will be maximum reflected signal and maximum height of the corresponding signal as it appears on the A-scope. For example, the 15-mile target may show a maximum vertical height when the antenna is pointed 30 degrees off of the ship's heading. At this time the 32-mile target may not be on its peak.

To find the bearing of the 32-mile target, it is necessary to continue the antenna orientation until there is maximum deflection of this echo on the screen. For example, the 32-mile signal may not reach its maximum until the antenna is directed at an angle

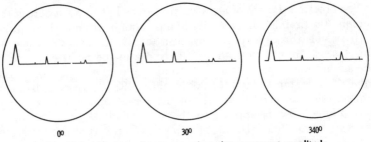

Fig. 1-13. Influence of antenna orientation on target amplitude.

of 340°. At this angle the signal from the 15-mile target, you will notice, has fallen away from its peak value.

1-10-2. Plan-Position-Indicator (PPI) Display

Range and bearing are displayed on the PPI screen. The basic PPI presentation is a circular one that is traced out by a rotating sweep line, as shown in Fig. 1-14. The very center of the round screen is the origin of the trace and corresponds to the position of the radar installation.

As the antenna rotates in a PPI radar installation the angular position of the sweep line indicates the azimuth angle of the antenna. In fact, the PPI trace line rotates (15 to 30 rpm) in a synchronism with the antenna, always indicating the azimuth angle or bearing of the antenna relative to a zero reference angle.

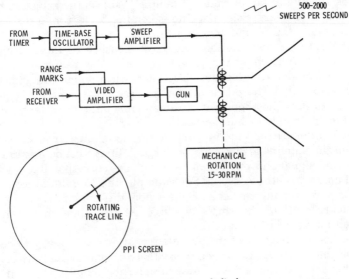

Fig. 1-14. PPI type of display.

24

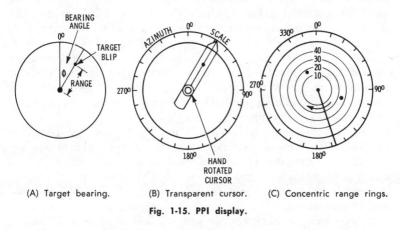

(A) Target bearing.   (B) Transparent cursor.   (C) Concentric range rings.

Fig. 1-15. PPI display.

The reference angle can be the ship's heading. In other installations the reference angle can be true north.

The trace line as it rotates causes some illumination of the screen. An arriving target signal causes a brighter illumination of the screen. The return target signals are applied to the electron gun of the radar cathode-ray tube and cause intensity modulation of the beam. It can be compared to the influence of a video signal applied to the grid of a television picture tube.

If a target is painted on the screen by the rotating trace line, as in Fig. 1-15, its angular position on the display tube shows the

Courtesy Radio Corporation of America

Fig. 1-16. Small-boat radar showing PPI screen and azimuth scale.

target bearing. Often a transparent cursor is included. It can be hand rotated until its hairline, as shown in Fig. 1-15B, crosses the target and sets off the bearing on the azimuth scale that surrounds the periphery of the display tube (Fig. 1-16).

The range of the target is disclosed by the distance separation between the target and the center of the display. A target at maximum range would appear at the edge of the display. A nearer target would be painted on the screen by the rotating trace line nearer to the origin.

Like the A-scope presentation, the PPI display can be range calibrated. Instead of vertical marks the range calibrations are set off by concentric circles referred to as range rings. Again, assuming a 40-mile range, it is possible that there would be four concentric rings, as in Fig. 1-15C, setting off the 10-, 20-, 30-, and 40-mile ranges.

In the example there are two targets. One appears at a bearing of 330° and is approximately 18 miles away. A second target at 25 miles has a bearing of approximately 110°.

The PPI radar system does not only pick out a few isolated targets; rather, it picks up any target capable of returning a signal, so long at that target is within the useful range of the radar set. The targets are painted on the screen regardless of their bearing. In fact, a PPI presentation is almost map-like.

A radar picture of New York harbor is shown in Fig. 1-17. Make a comparison between what is seen on the radar screen and a map of the same area. Your location, at the center of the radar screen, corresponds to a position on New York's East River. In fact, you have just passed under the Manhattan and Brooklyn bridges and are moving between the edge of Manhattan and Governor's Island. Notice how the radar sets off the land masses with a large area of illumination. The water area is dark. The docks can be distinguished along the shore lines.

Another typical PPI presentation is shown in Fig. 1-18. This type of pattern can be seen in moving along a bay or inland waterway. The actual buoys along the channel can be seen. The radar shows other small boats moving along the channel; shore line and bridges stand out clearly.

In summary, the PPI screen is ideal for shipboard radar because of its map-like type of display. Aircraft radar use the PPI display for the same reason. Likewise land-based radar that must keep watch on aircraft traffic in all directions can make good use of the circular display. Although the PPI is by far the most common type of display, there are specific uses for other types in such applications as weather radar, aircraft landing, missile tracking, etc.

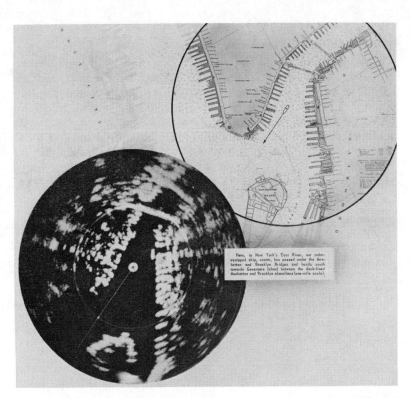

Here, in New York's East River, our radar-equipped ship, center, has passed under the Manhattan and Brooklyn Bridges and heads south towards Governors Island between the dock-lined Manhattan and Brooklyn shorelines (one-mile scale).

Courtesy Raytheon Co.

Fig. 1-17. Harbor display.

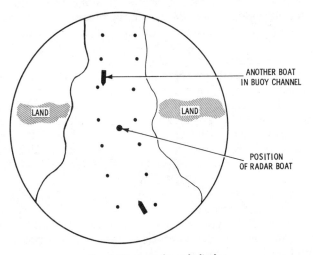

ANOTHER BOAT
IN BUOY CHANNEL

LAND

LAND

POSITION
OF RADAR BOAT

Fig. 1-18. Buoy-channel display.

1-10-3. B- and C-Type Scans

Two other basic scans are shown in Fig. 1-19. In both systems the return echo signal is applied to the grid-cathode circuit of the radar tube, and intensity modulation of the beam similar to the PPI presentation is caused. However, a scanning raster is traced on the radar screen. This raster is similar to the lined raster that can be seen on a television picture-tube screen with the exception that the lines are vertical instead of horizontal.

Usually the presentation is adjusted so that the lines only faintly show. When an echo signal arrives, it causes a brighter illumination of one particular point on the raster.

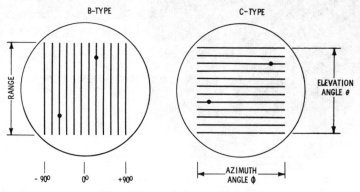

Fig. 1-19. B- and C- type displays.

In B-scan the vertical motion of the scanning beam corresponds to the target range. Thus the scanning beam as it moves from bottom to top of the display has a timing that corresponds to the round-trip excursion for a radar pulse in traveling out to and back from a maximum range target. This action is similar to the A-scan method with the exception that the motion of the scanning beam is vertical instead of horizontal.

The vertical coordinate of the presentation is calibrated in range. The horizontal is the azimuth coordinate and corresponds to the bearing of the antenna. For this type of scan the antenna usually covers a 90-degree sweep on each side of dead ahead. In so doing, the blip as it appears on the radar screen indicates both the range and bearing of the target.

The C-type display is similar but displays the elevation angle of the target and the azimuth angle instead of the range and azimuth angle. This type of radar is generally used for tracking, because it displays the horizontal (azimuth) and vertical (elevation) angles of the target.

28

1-11. PPI FUNCTIONAL BLOCK DIAGRAM

Some of the basic principles and a major unit block diagram of a PPI radar system were covered in Sections 1-9 and 1-10. Additional understanding is gained by considering the functional breakdown of each of the major units that comprise the PPI system. The breakdown will be in four sections: timer, transmitter-modulator, receiver, and indicator.

1-11-1. Timer

The timer, or synchronizer (Fig. 1-20), is the timing center of the radar system. Often a stable sine-wave oscillator is operated at the pulse-repetition frequency of the radar system. The output sine wave is applied to a limiter-clipper circuit which forms a squared wave. A follow-up differentiating circuit shapes the square wave into a pulse.

Fig. 1-20. Block diagram of a radar timer.

The actual trigger or timing pulse is formed in one of two ways. The differentiated pulse itself can be further shaped to form a steep-sided and short-duration pulse that can act as a trigger. In an alternate arrangement the pulse can be used to synchronize a blocking oscillator or multivibrator. This generator, in turn, forms the steep-sided timing trigger.

How is the timing trigger pulse used? (1) It is supplied to the modulator where it synchronizes the generation of the modulator pulse that eventually fires the magnetron. (2) It is supplied to the indicator where it initiates the trace portion of the CRT sweep. Hence, the start of the trace on the screen coincides with the transmit pulse. (3) It triggers the range-mark generator which forms the special calibration signals that place the range rings on the PPI display. (4) It triggers various other special circuits according to the design features and intended application of the particular radar set.

1-11-2. Transmitter-Modulator

The transmitter-modulator generates the microwave pulse sent out by the antenna. The basic functions of the transmitter and associated duplexer were stated in the discussions associated with the block diagrams of Figs. 1-9 and 1-10. The block plan of the modulator section is shown in Fig. 1-21.

The modulator generates the high-powered switching pulse needed to turn on the magnetron oscillator an exact number of times each second. In generating the high-powered microwave burst, the magnetron anode-cathode voltage (when in oscillation) must be thousands of volts, and the magnetron tube must draw a high peak current. In fact, because of magnetron and other circuit losses, the power in the pulse that turns the magnetron on and off must be greater than the RF output of the magnetron. Thus a radar modulator uses high-power and high-voltage components.

The basic modulator-control pulse is usually generated by a multivibrator that is synchronized by the timing trigger. The generated pulse, after amplification and shaping, is used as a thyratron trigger. High-powered switching is the responsibility of the thyratron.

When the radar is listening, the modulator power supply stores up energy in a special network. When the transmit pulse is to go out, the thyratron fires, and in so doing the energy stored in the network is released as a high-voltage and high-powered pulse to the magnetron. The magnetron oscillates and sends out the transmit pulse. The network and thyratron switch are designed to turn on the magnetron quickly, hold it on for a specific pulse duration, and then shut it down quickly.

1-11-3. Receiver

The receiver (Fig. 1-22) amplifies and demodulates the returning target signal. Usually the same antenna is used for transmit and receive. Sometimes a separate receive antenna is positioned near the transmit antenna.

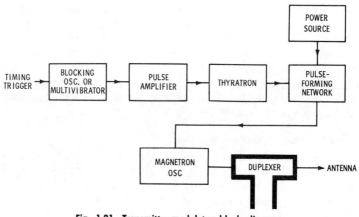

Fig. 1-21. Transmitter-modulator block diagram.

The receiver can be a single unit. Often it is in two parts, the RF head mounted at the antenna and the other part of the receiver at the indicator.

The RF head usually includes a crystal mixer, a klystron local oscillator, and two or more stages of IF amplification. Additional IF amplifier stages are included in the second part of the receiver. In recent years, tunnel diodes, transistors, and other solid-state devices have become more common in microwave equipment. Microwave tubes and other special circuits are covered in Chapter 2.

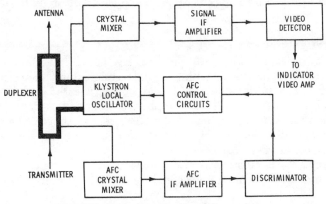

Fig. 1-22. Block diagram of a radar receiver.

Two crystal mixers are generally used. One crystal mixer supplies target IF signals to the high-gain IF amplifier. The bandwidth must be such that the return target signals will not be distorted and will therefore appear as bright and distinct blips on the radar screen. After IF amplification the target signal is demodulated by an AM video detector. The demodulated signal is increased in magnitude and applied to the indicator circuit.

The second crystal mixer is used for automatic frequency control (AFC). It makes certain that the receiver displays a maximum sensitivity to returning target signals by keeping the klystron on the proper frequency. In so doing, the target signal is always converted to the desired IF frequency.

The magnetron frequency may drift, and therefore the difference frequency between the returning target signal and the local-oscillator frequency may not match the IF frequency of the receiver. It is the responsibility of the AFC system to keep the oscillator frequency tracking any change in magnetron frequency. Therefore the difference frequency will always be the exact IF frequency.

In the AFC crystal mixer a small component of the transmit pulse is compared with a signal component from the local oscillator. The difference frequency is amplified in a second IF amplifier and applied to a discriminator. If there is any drift in the frequency of the transmit pulse, there will be a change in the DC voltage at the output of the discriminator. This "error" voltage is then used to control the frequency of the klystron local oscillator. The change in frequency is such that the local oscillator follows any change in transmit frequency and maintains a constant IF frequency output. By so doing, the return signal is ensured of maximum amplification in the signal IF amplifier of the receiver.

1-11-4. Indicator

The indicator (Fig. 1-23) and its associated cathode-ray tube process the various incoming signals and display them on the radar screen. A demodulated target signal, referred to as a video signal, is amplified and then applied to the grid-cathode circuit of the radar CRT. By varying the CRT beam strength, the signal causes an illuminated bright mark to appear on the fluorescent screen of the radar tube.

Range-mark pulses are also generated in the indicator. They are, of course, formed under synchronization of the trigger pulses

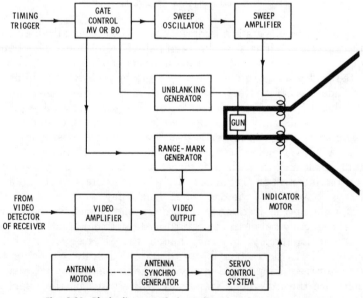

Fig. 1-23. Block diagram of the indicator and servo system.

from the timer. These pulses are mixed in the video amplifier with the incoming return signal; both signals are then applied so as to intensity-modulate the beam of the radar display tube.

In the radar display it is necessary to turn off the scan beam during retrace from the outer periphery of the screen back to the center, prior to the start of a new trace. In the indicator circuit, so-called gating or blanking pulses are used to turn off the radar scanning beam during the retrace time.

Still another function of the indicator is to generate the sweep waveform that is applied to the deflection coil of the radar tube. This waveform causes the trace motion of the beam from the center of the radar tube out to the periphery. This trace motion must begin in synchronism with the transmitted pulse. Furthermore, the velocity with which the beam moves from the center to the outer part of the screen must correspond to the travel time of the radar pulse for the particular range setting. Consequently the generation of the sweep waveform must also be synchronized by the trigger pulse.

One final responsibility of the indicator circuit is to cause the scanning line to revolve about the PPI display in synchronism with the rotation of the antenna. The servo system shown in Fig. 1-23 has this responsibility. The antenna is rotated by a motor. Associated with the rotation of the antenna is a synchro generator. Its signal, through a servo system, controls a servo motor back at the indicator. The indicator motor, in turn, rotates the deflection coil of the radar display tube. When properly phased, the rotation of the deflection coil follows the rotation of the antenna.

Usually when the antenna is pointing dead ahead, the trace line on the display tube is directed upward. As the antenna rotates, the trace line itself rotates around the display screen because the deflection coil is rotated by the synchro motor.

1-12. Summary

Chapter 1 has covered the basic principles of radar. The general operation was covered in the form of functional block diagrams. As you go over the questions and answers associated with Chapter 5 you will find that many of the answers are referenced to this chapter. The chapter is very important in that it gives you a basic understanding of radar and the basic information for answering a high percentage of the FCC study guide questions pertaining to radar.

CHAPTER 2

Circuits and Components

In this chapter the key circuits and components of a radar set will be discussed in more detail than in the previous chapter. This material will be particularly helpful in preparing for the radar license endorsement examination.

2-1. WAVE GUIDES AND ANTENNAS

A particular advantage of microwave transmission is that the microwave energy can be concentrated into a pencil-like beam with an antenna of practical dimensions. As mentioned in Chapter 1, a highly directional beam is important in obtaining an accurate bearing and a bearing resolution that will permit the radar operator to delineate closely spaced targets.

A problem of microwave transmission is that the signal must be handled carefully to minimize losses. The attenuation and radiation losses of a conventional coaxial or flat-type transmission line are excessive above 1000 megacycles. These losses increase with frequency. Occasionally, for short spans, very high-quality coaxial lines are used on operating frequencies up into the medium-microwave spectra. However, by far the most efficient transmission line is the wave guide, which is a single hollow metal conductor (Fig. 2-1). Wave guides may be rectangular, round, or oval; the rectangular type is the most common.

2-1-1. Wave Guides

Microwave energy travels within the metal enclosure of a wave guide by bouncing off the inner walls. There is no significant

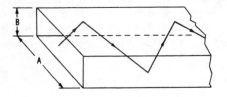

Fig. 2-1. A wave guide.

penetration of the walls and, consequently, no radiation loss. In fact the waves are reflected off the inner walls with little attenuation loss. Thus the waves propagate along the guide with very little loss, even as compared to the current losses encountered by a lower-frequency wave traveling along a conventional transmission line.

The transmission of microwave energy along a wave guide is in the form of electromagnetic propagation, just as a wave is propagated through space, except that the radiation is confined within the guide. In considering the operation of a wave guide, therefore, we are concerned with magnetic and electric lines of force. These hold the same significance as the RF current and voltage distribution along a regular transmission line.

You are aware that there are *electric lines of force* between the plates of an operating capacitor, as in Fig. 2-2. There are *mag-*

—— ELECTRIC
— — MAGNETIC

ELECTRIC LINES
BETWEEN PLATES

MAGNETIC LINES
ABOUT A CONDUCTOR
CARRYING CURRENT

TEM MODE IN A
COAXIAL CABLE OR
RESONANT CIRCUIT

Fig. 2-2. Electric and magnetic fields.

netic lines of force about a current-carrying conductor. In the case of an actual coaxial transmission line there are electrostatic lines of force between the inner and outer conductors, and a magnetic field is set up about the current-carrying wire. In this case the magnetic lines are confined within the outer conductor.

From the preceding it is apparent that there are both electric and magnetic lines of force in the air or other dielectric material between the inner and outer conductors of a coaxial line. These lines of force are perpendicular to each other and are perpendicular to the direction of current flow in the line, as shown in Fig. 2-2. The electrostatic field configuration for such a coaxial line is said to be transverse electromagnetic (TEM), because both fields are normal to the direction of wave travel. The transverse electromagnetic mode of operation is common to all types of transmission lines except wave guides.

In the transmission line the two conductors provide a return path for field energy. A wave guide has only one conductor. There is no physical return path for the RF energy. The changing lines of force must provide the continuous movement and completed loops within the guide. Either the electric or the magnetic field must be oriented in part in the direction of propagation. Since the electric and magnetic fields are always perpendicular to each other, both fields cannot be perpendicular to the direction of propagation. Thus the TEM mode is impossible in a wave guide.

There are two basic modes of wave-guide propagation. One is called transverse electric (TE) because the electric field is perpendicular to the direction of propagation (Fig. 2-3). The magnetic field in this case is parallel to the direction of propagation. In the transverse (TM) mode the magnetic field is perpendicular to the direction of propagation, while the electric field parallels the direction of propagation.

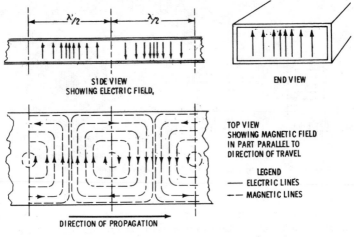

SIDE VIEW
SHOWING ELECTRIC FIELD.

END VIEW

TOP VIEW
SHOWING MAGNETIC FIELD
IN PART PARALLEL TO
DIRECTION OF TRAVEL

LEGEND
—— ELECTRIC LINES
– – – MAGNETIC LINES

DIRECTION OF PROPAGATION

Fig. 2-3. Transverse electric (TE$_{10}$) mode.

There are various subdivisions of the TE and TM basic modes. These are indicated by two subnumerals which indicate the number of amplitude peaks that fall along the long or short walls of the wave guide. The first subnumeral indicates the number of patterns or half periods that fall along the long walls of the rectangular guide (side-to-side A dimension of Fig. 2-1). The second subscript indicates the number of patterns or half periods that fall along the short walls from top to bottom (B dimension in Fig. 2-1).

In the case of the TE mode, these patterns are electric field patterns; for the TM mode, they are magnetic field patterns. In the example of Fig. 2-3 the mode is TE$_{10}$, indicating that the electric field pattern shows one pattern from side to side and is uniform from top to bottom.

Several other modes are shown in Fig. 2-4. In the TE_{20}, notice that the half-period pattern repeats twice. For the TE_{11} mode there is a pattern along both walls. The TM_{11} is similar except that it is a magnetic field pattern along both walls.

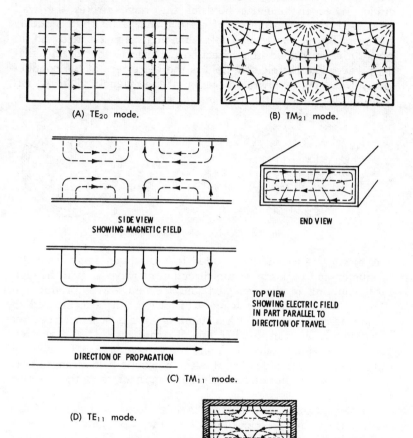

(A) TE_{20} mode.

(B) TM_{21} mode.

SIDE VIEW
SHOWING MAGNETIC FIELD

END VIEW

TOP VIEW
SHOWING ELECTRIC FIELD
IN PART PARALLEL TO
DIRECTION OF TRAVEL

DIRECTION OF PROPAGATION

(C) TM_{11} mode.

(D) TE_{11} mode.

Fig. 2-4. Other wave-guide modes.

Circular wave guides also have specific uses in radar systems. A circular wave guide is frequently associated with the waveguide feed to a rotating antenna. Two basic circular modes are shown in Fig. 2-5. For the circular wave guide the first numerical subscript refers to the number of full-period patterns around the wave guide, while the second subscript indicates the number of half-period patterns between the center of the guide and the outer wall. Proper modes must be selected with respect to those points at which energy is transferred between circular and rectangular wave-guide sections.

In the propagation of a wave along a wave guide it is the reflections off the sidewalls that permit the wave to move along the guide. When the electric field of the wave strikes the wall (Fig. 2-6), there is a motion of electric charges at the conductor surface. This motion results in a changing magnetic field and, in turn, an electric field of a direction opposite to that of the incident wave. The net electric field is therefore zero at the conduction surface. However, the direction of the magnetic field is such that it adds to that of the incident wave.

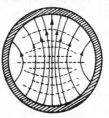

TE$_{11}$ TM$_{01}$

Fig. 2-5. Circular wave-guide modes.

A new wave is now propagated in a direction away from the conductor and opposite to the direction of wave arrival. In fact, the combining of the reflected and incident waves produces a standing electromagnetic wave. This wave can be compared to the mechanism that produces a standing wave on a shorted section of conventional transmission line. In this case, at the shorted point the current is maximum and the voltage is zero. In the case of the electromagnetic wave, it is the magnetic field strength that is maximum at the surface of the conductor, and the electric field is zero.

If a second conducting surface is now placed in the path of the wave, as it is by the opposite wall of the wave guide, the wave will again be reflected from the second side. When the spacing between the two conducting walls is exactly one-half wavelength, the RF energy will bounce back and forth between the conductors. However, it will not propagate along the conductor length.

From the discussion it is obvious that if the wave is to bounce from wall to wall and, at the same time, propagate along the guide, a wave guide must be dimensioned correctly and excited by the proper mode. The microwave energy must be made to strike the wall at an angle. Since the angle of reflection is equal to the angle of incidence, the energy can be made to move along

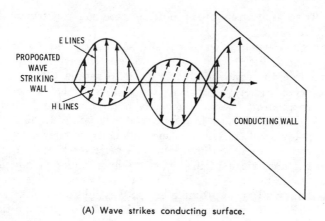

(A) Wave strikes conducting surface.

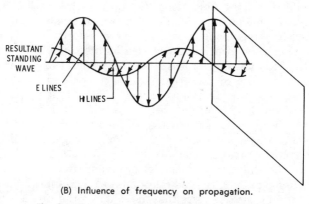

(B) Influence of frequency on propagation.

Fig. 2-6. Propagation of energy along a wave guide.

the line, as shown in Fig. 2-6B. The number of times that the energy is reflected from the wall in a given distance along the guide is determined by its wavelength and the dimension A of the guide. As the wavelengths become shorter (higher microwave frequency) for a given dimension (A), the fewer are the reflections from the wall. As the wavelength increases (lower frequency), the incidence and reflection angles approach zero, and there is a closer spacing between the points of refraction. At the frequency for which the wave-guide dimension A is a half wavelength, the waves reflect back and forth; there is no propagation down the guide. This is referred to as the cutoff frequency of the wave guide.

At frequencies lower than the cutoff frequency, the microwave wavelength is greater than the half wavelength dimension of the guide. The signal attenuates rapidly to zero a short distance from the entrance.

A lower frequency wave can be accommodated by using a larger wave guide; however, this imposes a practical limitation. For example, the width of a wave guide to handle a 900-mc wave must be approximately 7 inches. Hence wave guides are not used at low frequencies, except for costly high-powered installations.

For higher microwave frequencies the wave-guide dimensions can be made smaller. Thus, at several thousand megacycles and higher, the wave-guide dimensions are very small and practical. In general, the width of the wave guide is seldom made much greater than one wavelength. For optimum operation the inside width (long wall) is approximately 0.8 λ, while the height (short wall) is 0.38 λ. In so doing the dominant TE_{10} mode condition is set up with one pattern repeat along the long wall and an essentially uniform electric field along the short wall.

The group and phase velocities are two interesting properties of a wave moving along a guide. Group velocity refers to the speed at which the information carried by the signal travels down the guide. This velocity is less than the velocity of the wave in free space, because of the greater distance covered by the wave as it zigzags side-to-side along the walls. Thus, radar pulse information travels along a guide more slowly than in free space. The higher the frequency of the wave, the fewer are the reflections. Hence for a given wave-guide dimension, the group velocity is greater at higher frequencies.

On the other hand, the phase velocity is greater than the speed of light. For example, the actual points of maximum field intensity for individual RF cycles that move down the line are widely spaced. This faster motion of the individual cycles is suggested by the standing-wave pattern on a wave guide. In this case the spacing between two adjacent maxima is greater than a half wavelength in free space, indicating greater phase velocity.

The velocity factor is of practical significance in cutting a wave guide for a specific number of wavelengths. A wave guide must be cut longer than the calculated free-space wavelength. A conventional transmission line, you will recall, must be cut shorter than the calculated free-space wavelength of the signal transmitted along the line.

In summary, a wave guide provides complete shielding and therefore eliminates radiation loss. There is only one large-area conductor, and its inner wall resistance is low. As the wave moves along the guide, the reflections from the wall are almost complete, and there is little attenuation. The peak power handling capability is high. Because of the high microwave frequencies and the high peak power of the radar pulse, the wave guide is the preferred means of conveying both the signal from the microwave oscillator to the antenna, and also the return signal from the antenna to the receiver input.

A possible disadvantage of a wave guide is its size. However, at microwave frequencies these dimensions are quite practical. Installation is more difficult because bends and joints are of a more complicated nature than for conventional transmission lines.

2-1-2. Wave-Guide Accessories

Wave guides present various mechanical problems. Bends, turns, and joints can be made, but they must be planned carefully to provide a gradual and smooth transition along the path of

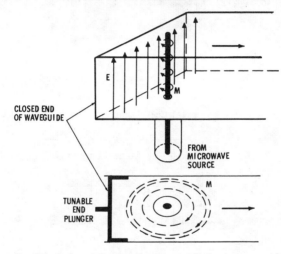

Fig. 2-7. Probe used to excite TE_{10} mode in a wave guide.

propagation. Bends should be beveled or have a large radius of curvature. In so doing discontinuities and harmonics are not introduced into the particular mode configuration. Flange joints are common; they must be smooth and tight fitting.

There must also be a means of transforming energy from a signal source to the guide. In such a transformation the wave guide must be excited at the proper mode.

Most microwave tubes, such as magnetrons and klystrons, as well as TR and ATR tubes, have wave-guide inputs and outputs. Hence, it is possible to use a flange joint. Some microwave tubes employ coaxial input and/or output. In this case it is necessary to use a probe excitation arrangement, such as shown in Fig. 2-7. An extension of the inner conductor of the coaxial segment

41

extends probe-like into the wave guide. Its electric field is parallel to the probe. Consequently, the electric vector in the wave guide becomes parallel with its short sides and transverse to the long side and the direction of propagation. Oppositely, the magnetic lines of force from the probe, although normal to the electric lines, are parallel to the direction of propagation. In this arrangement, therefore, the wave guide is excited in the TE_{10} mode.

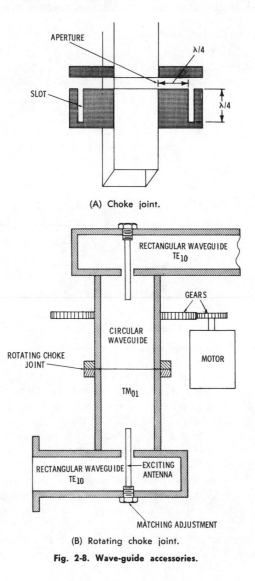

(A) Choke joint.

(B) Rotating choke joint.

Fig. 2-8. Wave-guide accessories.

Choke joints, such as that shown in Fig. 2-8, provide a smooth, tight fit. A choke joint has a flat and a slotted flange. The entire length of the section, from the aperture in the wall of the wave guide to the shorted end in the slotted flange, is exactly one-half wavelength. Since a shorted half-wavelength section of line reflects a short to its opposite end, the aperture between the two sections at the wave-guide wall is an electrical short circuit which maintains near-perfect electrical continuity along the wave-guide wall at the radar microwave frequency.

A rotating choke joint is shown in Fig. 2-8B. The rotating joint is again a choke type having a flat and a slotted section; one is fixed and the other rotates. In the arrangement despite some slight

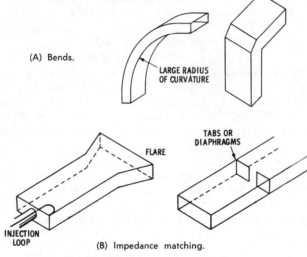

(A) Bends.

LARGE RADIUS OF CURVATURE

FLARE

TABS OR DIAPHRAGMS

INJECTION LOOP

(B) Impedance matching.

Fig. 2-9. More wave-guide accessories.

mechanical separation between the two flanges, the electrical continuity is sustained by the choke-joint arrangement. In fact, separations up to as high as several millimeters can be used without a serious disturbance of the energy being propagated along the guide. Two probe arrangements make the necessary transfers between rectangular and circular wave-guide segments. The TE_{10} mode transfer can be made with the simple arrangement of Fig. 2-8B.

Appropriate accessories can be used to match impedance. Several typical arrangements are shown in Fig. 2-9. Tabs or diaphragms can be inserted right into the wave guide. When dimensioned correctly and inserted at the proper positions, these tabs or diaphragms provide an impedance transformation.

Wave guides must also transfer signals to the radar antenna. Sometimes the open end of the wave guide is a source of radiated signal for a parabolic reflector. A better match and proper excitation or "illumination" of the reflector can be accomplished by tapering the end of the wave guide into a horn. Even a coaxial line can be used to excite such a wave-guide horn. In this case the inner conductor of the coaxial line extends as a loop into the wave-guide radiator.

Wave guides can be cut at specific lengths to serve as open- or short-circuits, or they can be made to display capacitive or inductive reactances. In association with diaphragms or external sections, wave guides can be made to have the characteristics of traps, bandpass filters, or band-rejection filters. In fact, a properly dimensioned wave-guide section can be made to operate as a series or parallel resonant circuit, just as transmission-line sections can be made to serve similar functions.

As shown in Fig. 2-10, wave-guide segments can be closed off into various shapes and forms. These are all called resonant cavities. Typical dimensions are shown. The simplest resonant cavity can be made by closing off both ends of a half-wavelength section of a rectangular or circular wave guide. In so doing there will be a circulating magnetic field similar to the circulating RF current in a conventional tuned circuit. Such a wave-guide cavity can be excited by an inductance loop coming from a coaxial line or by a wave-guide coupling system via a slot or iris. A wave-guide cavity can be tuned by using either a plunger arrangement or capacitive slugs.

A wave-guide cavity can be made to have an exceptionally high Q (often in excess of 10,000), and it is inherently stable and

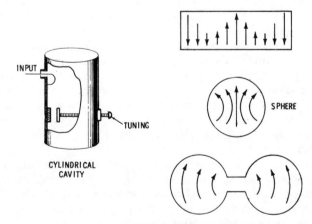

Fig. 2-10. Resonant cavities.

well shielded. When carefully calibrated in association with an accurate micrometer movement and scale, the wave-guide cavity can serve as an effective wavemeter for checking microwave frequencies and other parameters. The unit shown in Fig. 2-11 is calibrated between 11.5 and 13.2 kmc. It employs the plunger tuning and wave-guide flange method of inserting energy.

Courtesy Micro-Link Corp.

Fig. 2-11. Frequency wavemeter.

2-1-3. Radar Antennas

The parabolic reflector and wave-guide horn (Fig. 2-12) constitute the basic radar antenna. The microwave pulse is directed onto a parabolic reflector from the expanding aperture (horn) at the end of the wave guide. The horn taper matches the small wave guide to the surrounding space; its length and flair angle influence the radiation and gain characteristics of the antenna system.

The shape of the parabolic reflector is controlled in a manner that concentrates the RF energy into a single source of radiation that can then be sent out in a single direction. As shown in Fig. 2-12, there are equal angles of wave incidence and reflection at the parabolic surface. Thus, the rays coming off the reflecting surface flow outward in parallel paths. The energy coming off a full parabolic of this type is concentrated into a small-diameter pencil-like beam. The larger the parabolic antenna in terms of wavelength, the smaller the diameter of the beam is and the greater the antenna gain.

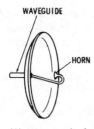

WAVEGUIDE

HORN

(A) Wave-guide fed.

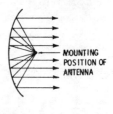

MOUNTING
POSITION OF
ANTENNA

(B) Wave reflection.

Fig. 2-12. Parabolic antenna.

Sectionalized parabolic reflectors are often employed if a circular beam is not required. Such sectionalized types generate beams of specific vertical and horizontal angles of radiation. At the same time, the physical dimensions of a sectionalized type can be made such that the sections are less awkward in terms of erection space and the need for location or scanning.

Parabolic-reflector diameters are at least several wavelengths and often ten or more wavelengths. Power gains of several thousand are practical.

In many radar services the horizontal radiation angle should be very narrow so as to have a good bearing resolution. However, it is often preferable for the vertical radiation angle to be substantially broader so as to minimize the vertical stability problem. For example, there is considerable vertical motion of a ship because of the waves. Hence it is very likely that a radar beam would swing above and below the target as the boat "rode the waves." However, this would not be so if the vertical beam from the antenna were rather wide. Hence a common antenna for shipboard radar would be a sectionalized parabola, as shown in Fig. 2-13. In terms of the horizontal beam width the parabolic section has a large diameter in terms of wavelength; therefore the beam is quite narrow. The height dimension of the reflector is limited, and therefore the vertical radiation angle is rather broad. Even

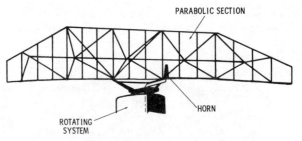

PARABOLIC SECTION

HORN

ROTATING
SYSTEM

Fig. 2-13. Parabolic section and rectangular horn illuminator.

the illuminating horn is an upright rectangle that helps establish a narrow horizontal angle and a wider vertical angle.

The antenna style of Fig. 2-14 is adaptable to marine radar, and it is referred to as a *pillbox*. The pillbox is a parabolic section positioned between two metal plates. The separation between the two plates can be somewhat less than one wavelength. The wave guide directs energy into the pillbox slot; the energy is then reflected from the parabolically shaped rear wall into a narrow horizontal beam. The vertical beam is rather broad, as is required for many practical radar applications.

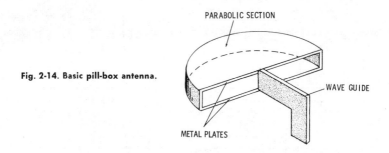

Fig. 2-14. Basic pill-box antenna.

Still another radar-antenna style is the slot antenna shown in Fig. 2-15A. Again it is long and narrow, which aids in the formation of the narrow horizontal beam and wider vertical beam. The long part of the antenna is a resonant extension of the wave guide. Radiating slots are cut into the guide at specific intervals. The long dimension of the slot makes it resonant to a specific microwave band. Each slot serves as a single radiator. A group of slots can be spaced to form an antenna that is composed of a number of phased radiating elements. Their radiated fields combine to form a high-gain, narrow-beam output.

A single slot of this type, as shown in Fig. 2-15B, is called a magnetic dipole because it is the changing *magnetic* field that constitutes the initial radiation. It can be compared with a conventional half-wavelength dipole. In the case of the dipole, the initial radiation is the result of a changing *electric* field.

As you know, a horizontal dipole generates a horizontally polarized wave. By this we mean the electric vector of the radiated wave is horizontal. To generate a horizontally polarized wave with a slot, it is necessary to use a vertical slot. In so doing the magnetic field is vertical and the resultant wave motion creates an electric vector that is horizontal, just as in the case of the horizontal dipole. Thus the vertical slot and the horizontal dipole generate the same type of electromagnetic wave.

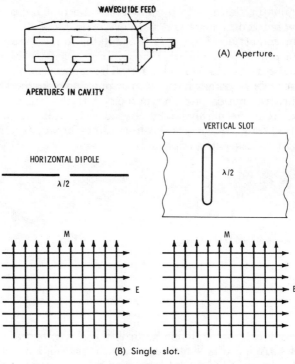

WAVEGUIDE FEED

(A) Aperture.

APERTURES IN CAVITY

VERTICAL SLOT

HORIZONTAL DIPOLE

λ/2

λ/2

M

M

E

E

(B) Single slot.

Fig. 2-15. Slot antenna.

2-2. SPECIAL TUBES

Conventional tubes and/or transistors can be used throughout most of the circuits of a radar set. However, there is a need for several special tube types. The FCC examination contains a number of questions on these special types that are used in radar sets.

2-2-1. Magnetron

The magnetron is the most common radar transmit tube. It is used almost exclusively in marine radar installations. Klystrons are sometimes used for extremely high-powered search-radar installations. The magnetron is a self-contained oscillator and requires only a means of input power application and RF microwave energy removal. Essential parts (Figs. 2-16 and 2-17) are the anode block and cathode mounted in an evacuated envelope, external magnet, and means for applying filament power and removing microwave energy. Following are some typical electrical data.

Heater Voltage ....5.0 Volts
Heater Current ....0.65 Amperes
Pulse Duration ....0.2 usec
Duty Cycle 0003
Peak Anode Voltage ....5.0 Kilovolts
Peak Anode Current ....3.5 Amperes
Peak Power Output ....5.0 Kilowatts
Frequency ....9410 ± 50 Mcs.
Life ....500 Hrs. Min.

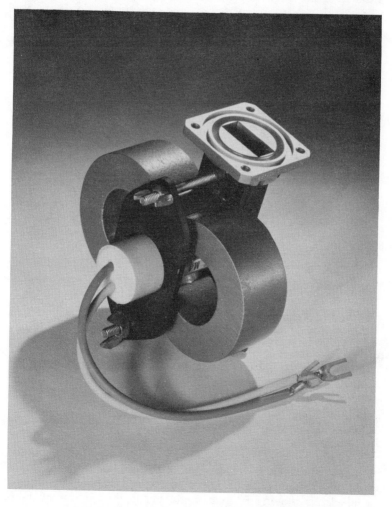

Fig. 2-16. Low-power magnetron for small plane and boat radar.

The anode block consists of a series of resonant cavities, each of which has the characteristics of a parallel resonant circuit. In approximation the holes function as inductances, and the slots function as capacitances. The cavities operate as individual resonant circuits connected in parallel. Therefore the total capacitance of the magnetron oscillator is nC (n = number of cavities), while the total inductance is L/n. Inasmuch as the resonant frequency of the magnetron varies inversely with the square root of the LC product, the frequency of the magnetron oscillator is the same as the resonant frequency of each individual cavity.

The multicavity arrangement and the unavoidable mutual coupling between cavities means that there are other resonant

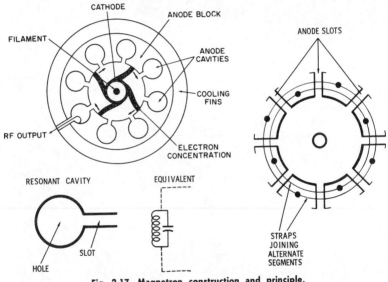

Fig. 2-17. Magnetron construction and principle.

modes. Thus the magnetron has stability problems, and it is possible that it may oscillate at other than the desired mode. This lack of stability and the tendency to oscillate at spurious modes are reduced with the technique of strapping, as shown in Fig. 2-17. In this arrangement every other resonant section is joined together with a segment of a circular ring. A second strap then joins the alternate set.

The cathode is positioned at the very center of the magnetron structure. Between the cathode and the anode block is the so-called interaction space. In this area there is interaction between the electrons moving from cathode to anode and the magnetic lines of force generated by a powerful external fixed magnet.

As shown in Fig. 2-18, heater power is supplied via a pulse transformer. The anode block forms the major portion of the outside area of the tube. For safety reasons it is usually grounded. Therefore, in pulsing the magnetron oscillator, it is necessary to use a pulse of a high negative amplitude which is applied to the cathode. Inasmuch as the anode operates at ground potential, the cathode and filament circuits must be designed to withstand a high negative potential. Filament chokes and transformer isolate the filament source from the pulse circuit.

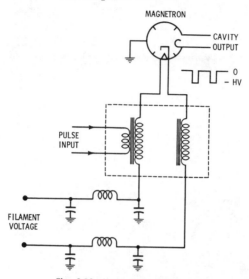

Fig. 2-18. Magnetron circuit.

Most magnetrons are fixed-tuned, with the frequency being determined by the physical dimensions of the cavity. Some slight change in frequency can be accomplished by varying the load into which the magnetron operates. Magnetrons can be tuned by mechanical means with the use of a bellows or a threaded arrangement. A frequency-changing inductive element can be made to move into the individual cavities, or a capacitive element can be inserted into the individual cavity slots.

Fundamentally, the magnetron oscillator is a transit-time or velocity-modulated type. The electrons released from the cathode come under the influence of various fields during the time that they are in transit between cathode and anode. These various fields cause a change in velocity among electrons and cause them to bunch as they come closer to the anode.

In understanding magnetron operation it is necessary to consider the influence of three fields. When the anode is positive with respect to the cathode, there is an electric field that draws the electrons in a straight line path between cylindrical cathode and the anode block (Fig. 2-19A).

In addition to the electric field there is a DC magnetic field established by the magnet. The influence of a magnetic field on an electron is to cause the electron to move in a direction normal to the magnetic field and its own surrounding magnetic field.

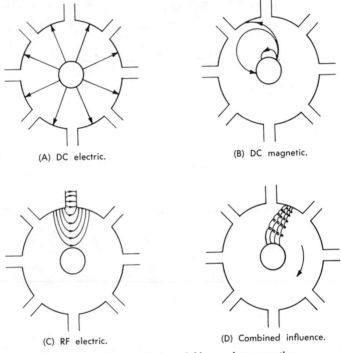

(A) DC electric.

(B) DC magnetic.

(C) RF electric.

(D) Combined influence.

Fig. 2-19. Influence of three fields on electron motion.

(When any electron is in motion, it has a surrounding magnetic field.) Thus, the electron would have a tendency to revolve in a circle were it not for the combined influence of the electric and magnetic fields, as shown in Fig. 2-19B. When the magnetic field is strong, it is dominant; thus when the electron leaves the cathode, it is turned around in a rather tight circle, returning to the cathode surface. For a somewhat weaker magnetic field the electron would continue to return to the cathode, but over a longer path. With a magnetic field of proper magnitude the electron has sufficient velocity, under the influence of the combined fields, to reach the anode block over a curved path.

In addition to the DC-electric and DC-magnetic fields, there is a radio-frequency (microwave) field which extends outward from the cavity slot, as shown in Fig. 2-19C. This is a fast-changing oscillating field that corresponds to the resonant frequency of the cavities.

As in the start of any type of oscillator, a finite time is required for the build-up. In the case of the magnetron oscillator, any slight discontinuity in electron flow becomes the catalyst that initiates the build-up of oscillations. The influence of the resultant RF fields is pronounced; they cause the electron velocities to build up and slow down. The relative influence the field exerts depends on the position from which a given electron leaves the cathode surface relative to the phase of the changing field. Thus, the RF field does not influence each electron to the same extent. As shown in Fig. 2-19D, the electrons are made to loop in transit between cathode and anode. The relative influence is such that the differing electron velocities cause the electrons to bunch together prior to their striking the anode, setting up the spoking of Fig. 2-17.

Furthermore, as the RF fields vary, the bunching activity revolves around the anode block like the spokes of a wheel. As the spokes revolve past the slots in the resonant cavities, bursts of energy are released, setting each cavity into oscillation. As you recall, in a vacuum tube and transistor oscillator the bursts of current flow (plate and collector currents, respectively) cause the output tuned circuit to oscillate. Similarly in the case of the magnetron, it is the cyclic bursts of energy delivered to the resonant cavities that sustain continuous oscillations.

In the case of a radar-pulsed magnetron these oscillations continue for the duration of the high-powered negative pulse applied to the cathode from the modulator. Between pulses there is no difference of potential between magnetron anode and cathode, and oscillations cease.

In normal magnetron operation a substantial number of electrons never reach the anode but are returned to the cathode surface. The bombardment of the cathode by these electrons produces additional heating and augments the filament power. In some magnetron circuits the filament power is actually removed once the electrons have taken over the heating of the cathode surface.

2-2-2. Klystron

The klystron is also a transit-time or velocity-modulated tube. It is a popular type of local oscillator for radar receivers. Klystrons are available with two resonant cavities or with a single resonant cavity. Klystron local oscillators are dominantly of the single-cavity type. However, we will first consider a two-cavity type because its operation can be more readily understood.

As shown in Fig. 2-20 the klystron consists of a cathode, accelerator grid, anode, and collector. With no voltages applied to the cavities, the electrons would move in a continuous stream from cathode to collector. In operation it is the cavity voltage variations that influence the electrons in transit between cathode and collector.

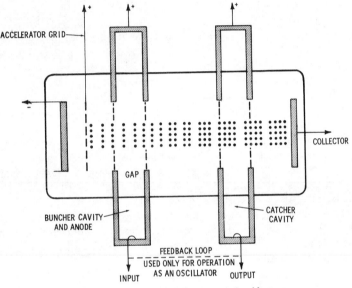

Fig. 2-20. Basic principle of a two-cavity klystron.

The electrons are first focused into a fine beam, and they pass into the first so-called buncher cavity through a hole in the anode. The electrons are acted on as they pass between the input and output sides of this cavity. In the case of klystron amplifier operation, the signal to the amplifier is applied across the two sides, or gap, of the cavity. In the case of an oscillator, it is the feedback voltage from the output cavity that appears across the sides of the first cavity.

As the far side of the gap swings positive with respect to the cathode side, the electrons in the beam are speeded up. During the negative alternation of the microwave signal the far side of the gap is negative with respect to the input side; consequently the electron velocity is slowed. It is apparent that as the microwave signal goes through its sinusoidal cycle at the first cavity,

54

there is a like change in electron velocity. In effect, the electron stream has been velocity modulated.

The electrons pass with differing velocities through the exit side into the so-called drift or bunching area. Inasmuch as they leave with differing velocities, the fast-moving electrons now have sufficient time to catch up to the slower-moving ones. Some of the very slow-moving electrons now fall back to the next group of fast-moving electrons.

Fig. 2-21. Klystron single-cavity oscillator.

Courtesy Raytheon Co.

From the preceding it can be seen that although the electrons left the cathode at a uniform velocity they now bunch together, as shown in Fig. 2-20. The electrons now pass the output-cavity gap in bunches. They deliver energy to that cavity at a cyclic rate, setting it into oscillation. Most of this power can be delivered to the output. Some of it must be fed back to the first cavity so that the electrons leaving the cathode will continue to be bunched. Oscillations can be sustained in this manner.

A single-cavity reflex klystron is shown in Figs. 2-21 and 2-22. The reflex klystron has only a single cavity, but a so-called repeller electrode or plate has been added. This electrode is operated at a negative potential with respect to the cathode.

An electron gun arrangement again acts as a source of electrons, directing them as a beam into the aperture area of the cavity. The acceleration given to the electrons is such that they continue to move toward the repeller plate despite its negative potential. However, the negative potential of the repeller plate has a retarding influence on the electrons. It causes them to slow down to zero velocity just ahead of the repeller plate. These slowed-down electrons are then attracted away from the repeller and back toward the positive gun area. They pass through the cavity again, but traveling in the opposite direction.

As in any oscillator circuit, a small variation will produce the necessary change in electron-current flow to initiate the build-up of oscillations. This weak RF variation influences the electrons of the beam as they pass through the aperture in the direction of the repeller plate. As in the case of the first cavity of the two-

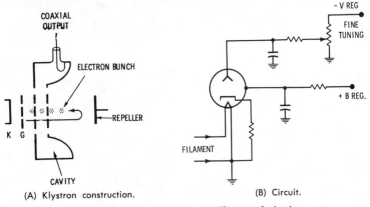

(A) Klystron construction.　　　(B) Circuit.

Fig. 2-22. Single-cavity klystron oscillator and circuit.

cavity klystron, the voltage variation across the cavity gap causes the electrons to speed up and slow down. The electron beam is again velocity modulated according to the RF voltage variation.

In traveling through the bunching area between the cavity aperture and the repeller plate, the differing velocities cause the electrons to arrive in bunches in front of the repeller plate.

The negative repeller reverses the direction of electron flow and causes the electrons to pass the gap again going in the opposite direction. Each bunch delivers energy to the resonant cavity, and in this manner, oscillations are sustained. Of course the resonant variations in the cavity are strong and some energy can be withdrawn via a pick-up loop or cavity output. Some energy must remain in the cavity to make certain that electrons leaving the gun continue to be bunched as they move toward the repeller.

It is apparent that the turn-about activity of the repeller plate permits the single cavity of the reflex klystron to act as both the output tank circuit and the buncher cavity.

A particular advantage of the klystron in terms of radar receiver operation is that its frequency can be changed in a simple manner. The frequency of operation of the reflex klystron, over a limited range, can be controlled with the negative repeller voltage. Actually the frequency of operation of the klystron oscillator depends on the rate of arrival of the returning electron bunches at the aperture. The faster the rate of arrival of the bunches, the higher the generated frequency is. The repeller plate can be used to control the spacing between electron bunches and, therefore, the ultimate frequency of operation.

When there is a highly negative repeller voltage, the electrons are returned earlier, because they drop to zero velocity a greater distance from the repeller plate. They therefore appear at the aperture at closely spaced intervals. As the repeller voltage is made less negative, the electron bunches travel a greater distance and come closer to the repeller before they are turned around. As a result they are in wider spaced bunches, and their rate of arrival at the aperture is slowed; hence, a lower microwave frequency of oscillation occurs.

As mentioned previously, radar systems often use an AFC system so that there might be a constant frequency difference between the transmit frequency and the local-oscillator frequency. This difference frequency must match the IF frequency for optimum receiver performance. The AFC system of a radar receiver compares magnetron and klystron frequencies and develops a DC error voltage that is applied to the repeller plate. Inasmuch as the repeller plate determines the klystron-oscillator frequency, any change in transmit frequency produces a corresponding change in the klystron local-oscillator frequency, thereby maintaining an exact IF frequency difference despite any drift in frequency of the magnetron oscillator.

2-2-3. TR and ATR Tubes

The TR and ATR tubes are a part of the duplexer described briefly in block diagram form in Chapter 1. The TR tube protects the receiver during the transmit pulse, and the ATR tube minimizes echo signal loss in the transmit channel during receive. Both tubes are gas-filled and contain two electrodes. The strong transmit pulse ionizes the gas and causes a low-resistance arc to develop between the two electrodes. In so doing, the TR and ATR tubes represent microwave-frequency short-circuits.

Usually they are mounted in a cavity and therefore the continuity of the wave guide or coaxial line system of the duplexer is maintained. They must also be positioned correctly to reflect the proper impedance to key points in the duplexer.

A typical duplexer and TR and ATR mounting position are shown in Fig. 2-23. The transmitter output sees a direct waveguide path through the duplexer to the antenna. In the receive channel the TR tube is mounted exactly one-quarter wavelength down from its T-junction connection to the wave guide. The transmit pulse fires the TR tube. Inasmuch as the TR tube then acts

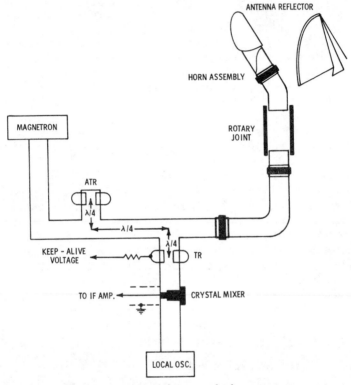

Fig. 2-23. Duplexer and antenna feed arrangement.

as a microwave short, it reflects a maximum impedance to the junction point. Therefore the transmit pulse sees a maximum impedance in the direction of the receiver. It does not enter the receiver channel but passes on to its antenna load.

The ATR tube is also fired by the transmit pulse. It reflects a high impedance (quarter-wavelength shorted) to its junction with the transmit path. Therefore, it does not impede the transmission of the pulse to the antenna.

The ATR tube performs its major task in the receive operation. When the transmit pulse is off and the receiver is listening, neither the TR nor the ATR tube is conducting. With the TR tube nonconducting, there is no opposition to the flow of receive signal into the receiver. Since the ATR tube is also open and is exactly one-half wavelength away from the entrance to the receive channel, it reflects a high impedance to this point. Thus an incoming signal sees a high impedance looking toward the magnetron. Therefore it does not enter the transmit channel. Rather it follows the low-impedance path to the receiver input.

TR and ATR tubes (Fig. 2-24) are quite similar except for a facility for applying a so-called keep-alive voltage to the TR tube. This is a negative voltage applied to the cathode of the TR tube. In a radar system it is very important that the receiver input be

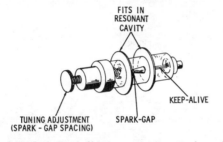

Fig. 2-24. Basic TR and ATR construction—No keep-alive facility for ATR.

blocked very quickly with the initiation of the transmit pulse. By so doing the receive detector and other components are not burned out or relegated to a short operational life. If this is to be accomplished, the TR tube must fire instantly at the start of the transmit pulse. The fast firing is insured by the keep-alive voltage. By maintaining a difference of potential across the electrodes, the gap is set almost to the very point of arcing. Hence, the tube fires immediately with the start of magnetron oscillation.

The gas content of the two tubes is not always the same. The gas make-up of the TR tube is optimized for fast starting and rapid deionization after the transmit pulse. A rapid deionization is required so that the receiver can be made ready quickly for the pick-up of a returning echo signal.

2-2-4. Radar Display Tubes

The cathode-ray radar display tubes are similar to those used in oscilloscopes and television receivers. An electron gun (Figs. 2-25 and 2-26) is used to form a small-diameter beam of electrons which is focused electrostatically or electromagnetically on to the fluorescent screen. A variety of fluorescent-screen types are avail-

able. Screen characteristics depend on the desired image reten-
tion, brightness, and viewing requirements. Radar tubes are available with internal electrostatic-deflection plates or external magnetic-deflection coils. In either case the sweep deflection rate
corresponds to the pulse repetition rate of the radar system.

For a PPI type of display the echo and range mark signals are
applied to the control grid of the electron gun. They cause an
increase in the beam current and brighter illumination of the

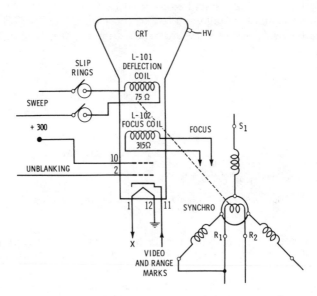

Fig. 2-25. PPI display using magnetic-deflection coil.

screen at the point where the beam is scanning when the signals
arrive. The revolving trace line causes some illumination of the
screen. The grid signals enhance this illumination. The signal
illumination is so bright that its corresponding segment of the
screen will continue to remain illuminated even after the trace
line has passed on. Each time the trace line passes the same point,
the brightness will be reinforced by the arriving signal and a
distinct target "blip" will be apparent.

How is the trace line revolved? The arrangement of Fig. 2-25
is typical. The deflection coil itself is made to rotate in synchronism
with the antenna, while the sweep current applied to the deflection coil has the same frequency as the pulse repetition rate. The
trace begins its sweep from the center of the screen in synchronism
with each transmit pulse. Hence, for a given direction and range

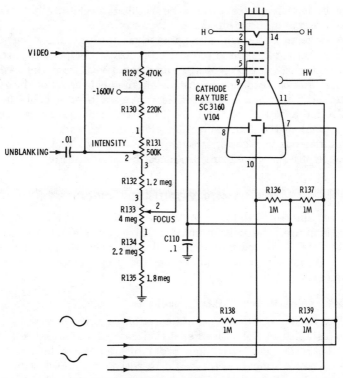

Fig. 2-26. Electrostatic-deflection radar tube.

of target the scanning beam will always be at exactly the same spot on the fluorescent tube when the signal from a particular target arrives at the control grid of the radar display tube. The arriving signal will continue to restore the brightness of its corresponding blip on the screen so long as a signal is being reflected from the target.

The activity just discussed occurs in exactly the same manner for all returning signals and range marks. As the trace line moves outward from the center and revolves simultaneously around the screen, each return signal reproduces as a blip. Thus, the PPI screen shows a map-like display of all signals received. The brightness of each individual blip is renewed for each rotation of the trace line. The display can be centered by external permanent magnets or separate external deflection coils.

Some radar tubes use a three-winding, nonrotating deflection-coil assembly. A proper three-phase signal will then produce a rotating trace line. A PPI display can also be produced by applying appropriate signals to deflection plates, as shown in Fig. 2-26.

The deflection plates cannot be rotated mechanically because they are mounted within the cathode-ray tube.

A deflection voltage is originated at the antenna. The same motor that rotates the antenna also revolves a wiper arm around a circular resistor. A voltage can be derived from the resistor circuit that corresponds to the instantaneous bearing of the radar antenna. This signal variation is conveyed over a cable to the deflection amplifier of the indicator. After suitable processing, it is applied to the four deflection plates of the radar scope tube. Simultaneously a sweep waveform is applied, and the net influence of both waveforms produces the rotating trace line.

2-3. TIMER-MODULATOR CIRCUITS

The timer-modulator circuits generate and shape the basic trigger pulse. The trigger pulse, in turn, initiates the generation of the high-powered modulator pulse which turns on the magnetron oscillator according to the desired pulse duration and repetition rate.

2-3-1. Sine-Wave Master Oscillator

The master oscillator generates either a sine wave or a pulse that establishes the pulse repetition rate of the radar set. This oscillator should have a high order of stability in terms of frequency, and in most cases, should be reasonably constant in terms of output voltage. Sine-wave, multivibrator, or blocking oscillators are used in this function.

Two typical sine-wave oscillators are shown in Fig. 2-27. Resistor-capacitor or RC sine-wave oscillators are stable in frequency and amplitude. A sine wave of good waveform (minimum harmonic content) can be generated without the need for costly inductors or transformers.

In any oscillator circuit it is required that a portion of the output be reversed in polarity and fed back in phase to the input. The RC phase-shift oscillator (Fig. 2-27A) uses either a three-section or a four-section resistor-capacitor network to obtain a net 180° phase shift. In a three-section arrangement each RC combination introduces a phase shift of 60°; in the less common four-section arrangement, each section contributes a 45° shift.

The high-stability of the phase-shift oscillator stems from the fact that a precise net phase-shift of 180° can only occur at one specific audio frequency. In the case of a three-section network there is only one frequency for which the ratio of reactance to resistance of each network will produce a 60° shift between the input and output signals.

(A) Phase-shift oscillator.

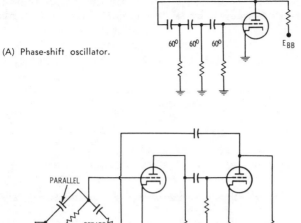

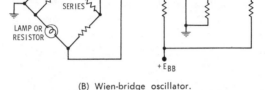

(B) Wien-bridge oscillator.

Fig. 2-27. Sine-wave oscillators.

Using this type of oscillator, the PRR of the radar can be switched from one repetition rate to another simply by switching either the three capacitors or the three resistors. Usually capacitor switching is employed.

Another type of phase-shift oscillator used in radar timers is the Wien-bridge type (Fig. 2-27B). This is a two-tube arrangement and the necessary feedback polarity shift is handled by the second tube. It is significant that with such a feedback plan and no bridge there would be a 180° phase shift over a rather wide span of audio frequencies. Stability would not be acceptable. Furthermore, the magnitude of the feedback could be such that relaxation oscillations would occur.

In the Wien-bridge arrangement a good sine waveform at some precise frequency is insured by the RC bridge network in the feedback path. The bridge is located between the output of the second stage and the input of the first stage. Note that a series RC combination is in the feedback path, while a parallel combination is across the input. The impedance of the series combination rises with frequency decline, while the impedance of the parallel combination falls with frequency rise. As a result, there is only one audio frequency at which the feedback is optimum for a given set of RC values. Actually this occurs at the frequency for which the ratio of output-to-input voltage is maximum. Frequency can be changed by switching capacitors and/or resistors.

The small lamp regulates the amplitude of oscillation by introducing a controlled amount of negative feedback. If there is a tendency for oscillations to increase, the AC current flow in the bulb becomes higher and increases the lamp resistance. In so doing there is a higher feedback factor and a resultant stabilization of the oscillator output level.

2-3-2. Shaping Circuits

As a first step in the formation of a trigger pulse, the sine-wave signal must be squared. This operation is performed by an overdriven stage, either a pentode or a pair of triodes. Both positive and negative alternations are limited and clipped drastically so as to form a steep-sided square wave (Fig. 2-28). Limiters in general operate with near-zero bias, although an appropriate grid RC combination is sometimes used to develop some additional signal bias. Often, low electrode voltages are used to obtain an early cutoff.

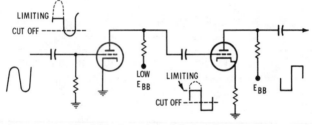

Fig. 2-28. Operation of limiter-clipper.

Customarily the first stage of a triode pair provides limiting action that removes almost the entire positive alternation of the sine wave which has been applied from the master sine-wave oscillator. There is also some cutoff clipping of the negative alternation. Thus, the first stage provides a considerable amount of squaring.

The output of the first stage is now of substantial amplitude, and it overdrives the second triode stage to such an extent that only a very small segment of the applied signal falls between the cutoff and limiting levels. This drastic clipping of a major part of the input wave develops an output square wave that has very steep, almost vertical, sides.

The next step in the formation of the pulse is to reduce the duration of the square wave and, at the same time, preserve its steepness. This can be accomplished with a so-called differentiating circuit composed of a simple series resistor-capacitor combination (Fig. 2-29). The time constant (product) of the RC combination is short compared to the duration of the square wave. As a result, in relation to the pulse period the capacitor charges and discharges quickly through the resistor.

When the pulse (1) is applied at time zero, its full amplitude appears immediately across the resistor (2). This happens because the capacitor has had *no time to charge*. It is significant then that the steep side of the pulse is developed immediately across the output. When the capacitor does begin to charge, it does so

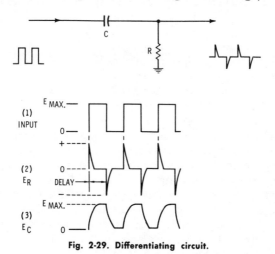

Fig. 2-29. Differentiating circuit.

quickly, because of the short time constant. At the start, current flow is maximum in the series circuit. In fact, it is this maximum current that has developed the leading edge (2) across the output.

The capacitor charges quickly to the peak amplitude of the pulse, as shown in the waveform (3). As it does, the current flow through the resistor decreases, because current flow in the series circuit is determined by the instantaneous difference of potential between maximum input pulse amplitude and instantaneous charge on the capacitor.

$$I = \frac{E_{max} - E_c}{R}$$

Hence, as the capacitor charges, both the series current flow and the voltage across the resistor decline at the same rate.

When the capacitor is charged to the peak amplitude of the pulse, current flow ceases and the voltage across the resistor drops to zero. It is apparent then that the output of the RC combination is a very much shorter duration waveform than the input pulse.

The same events repeat themselves at the trailing edge of the pulse. This time, however, the capacitor discharges to zero because of the opposite direction of voltage change during the trailing edge of the input pulse. A negative, instead of a positive, spike develops across the output resistor.

Either the positive or the negative spike can be used as a trigger by clipping off the spike not desired. In the example, the *positive spike is time coincident* with the leading edge of the input pulse.

The negative spike is said to provide a delayed trigger, the trigger being delayed relative to the leading edge by the time interval or duration of the input pulse. The latter technique is occasionally used to trigger some radar activity that must be delayed in its start so many microseconds after some other activity has been triggered by the leading edge of the pulse. There are various other pulse-delay methods which are covered in the discussion on radar systems.

In summary, the process of differentiation can be used to shape a pulse into a sharp short-duration trigger either coincident with the leading edge of the pulse or delayed a specific interval of time with respect to that edge.

A differentiated pulse of this type may be used directly as a timing trigger to synchronize a multivibrator (MV) or blocking oscillator (BO) which will then generate the actual modulator pulse. In more elaborate radar sets the differentiated pulse may only be used to synchronize a MV or BO that, in turn, generates the basic timing-trigger pulse that will be used throughout the radar system.

2-3-3. Multivibrators and Blocking Oscillators

Multivibrators and blocking oscillators are used in various forms in radar sets. Their operation can be controlled with a trigger pulse, or in a small radar set they may themselves serve as the timing oscillator instead of a sine-wave oscillator.

Multivibrators—Two basic multivibrator circuits are shown in Figs. 2-30 and 2-31. In Fig. 2-30A, tube V1 is RC-coupled to V2 and then the output of V2 is RC-coupled back to V1 input, thus providing the polarity shift that is needed to support oscillation. However, such an oscillator does not operate in a conventional manner because the feedback magnitude is such that the tubes are switched on and off alternately by the charge placed on the two grid time constants. In this manner a squared or other form of nonsinusoidal wave can be produced. This type of circuit is called a relaxation oscillator.

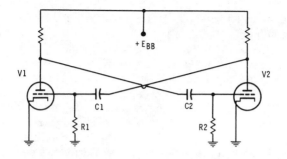

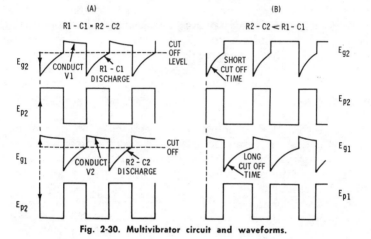

Fig. 2-30. Multivibrator circuit and waveforms.

When the two stages have the same component values the multivibrator is said to be symmetrical, and the various plate and grid waveshapes of the two stages are identical. In explaining the operation of any type of oscillator it is customary to assume some starting point. This is a valid assumption because there is no circuit that does not include some type of random noise or signal variation. From such a variation, tiny as it might be, starts the build-up which will eventually develop into continuous oscillations. No matter how hard we try to balance the two sections of a multivibrator there will always be some sort of unbalance. If there is any sort of unbalance, a cycle of events will evolve that will cause one tube to conduct and the other to cut off.

For these reasons we can assume, in explaining the operation of a multivibrator, that V1 is beginning to conduct and its grid voltage is rising. Consequently there is a corresponding increase in plate current and a fall in V1 plate voltage. This change, in turn, drives V2 grid negative and V2 plate positive. Since V2 plate is RC-coupled back to V1, there results an amplified increase in V1 grid voltage.

The net effect of this feedback activity is to drive V1 quickly positive to a limiting level and V2 quickly negative beyond cut-off. At this stage the feedback activity stops. However, still another change has occurred. The amplified feedback voltage has placed a high negative charge on capacitor C2, and before V2 can conduct again, this charge must leak off through resistor R2. In fact, tube V2 remains cut off and tube V1 conducts until the negative voltage being developed across R2 by the declining discharge current reaches the conduction level of V2. At this moment V2 plate current begins to rise and its plate voltage falls. In turn, V1 grid voltage swings negative and its plate voltage positive. There results a further increase in V2 grid voltage, and the feedback activity once again takes over. However, feedback is now of opposite polarity, with V1 being driven quickly to cut-off and V2 to the limiting level at which point a further increase in grid voltage will cause no additional increase in the plate current.

It is the R1-C1 time constant that now cuts off V1 and holds V2 conducting as capacitor C1 discharges through resistor R1. After an interval of time set by the time constant R1-C1, the grid of V1 reaches the conduction level and the entire cycle of activity begins to repeat.

The waveforms indicate that the actual period of the generated waveform corresponds to the sum of the V1 and V2 cutoff periods. Thus, the frequency of operation is determined to a great extent by time constants R1-C1 and R2-C2. If the time constants are equal, both tubes are cut off for the same time interval, and a symmetrical waveform (square wave) is developed in the plate circuit.

When a pulse output is desired, the time constants are made unequal, as shown in Fig. 2-30B. In so doing, one tube is cut off for a longer time interval than the other. In Fig. 2-30B, the R2-C2 time constant was reduced and the R1-C1 time constant increased like amount, relative to that of example Fig. 2-30A.

When the feedback activity drives V1 to cutoff, it remains cut off for a longer interval of time because it takes longer for C1 to discharge through R1 to the conduction level of V1. Note that the discharge time of R1-C1 in Fig. 2-30B is longer than in Fig. 2-30A. After V2 is driven to cutoff the charge on C2 discharges through R2 to the conduction level faster than in Fig. 2-30A. Thus V2 is cut off for a shorter time interval than V1 and, oppositely, V2 conducts for a longer period than V1. It is important to note that the multivibrator frequencies are the same in both examples; the difference is that the waves are symmetrical in one case and nonsymmetrical in the other.

The plate waveforms are interesting. Note that the short-duration positive pulse is available at the plate of V2 and a short-duration negative pulse at the plate of V1. In multivibrator and other pulse circuits a takeoff point can usually be found to obtain a pulse of a desired polarity.

The multivibrator of Fig. 2-31 is a cathode-coupled type. It differs from the previous type in that the feedback from V2 to V1 is by way of a common cathode resistor instead of a second RC-

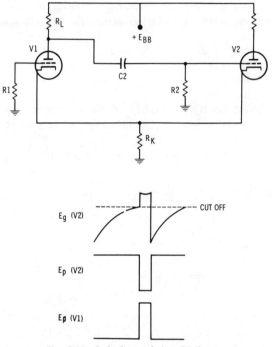

Fig. 2-31. Cathode-coupled multivibrator.

coupling combination. Thus, the only time constant circuit is R2-C2 associated with the grid circuit of V2.

If we assume V2 grid voltage is rising above cutoff, there will be a corresponding increase in V2 plate current. This current flow through the common cathode resistor decreases V1 plate current. The resultant increase in V1 plate voltage drives V2 to a limiting level.

With no supporting feedback because a further increase in V2 grid voltage causes no further drop in V2 plate voltage, V2 grid voltage begins to drop, V2 plate current decreases, and V1 plate current rises. Now the amplified negative swing of V1 plate voltage drives V2 grid beyond cutoff. The cutoff condition is now held until C2 discharges through R2 to the conduction bias level of V2. At this time a new cycle of events occurs as grid V2 begins to swing positive.

The cathode-coupled multivibrator has a capability of generating a short-duration pulse with fast leading and trailing edges. Note that a short-duration positive pulse is available at the plate of V1; a negative pulse, at the plate of V2. The frequency of operation is determined largely by the single R2-C2 time constant.

Blocking Oscillators—The blocking oscillator is also a common pulse generator used in radar systems. As shown in Fig. 2-32, feedback is by way of a transformer instead of a second stage. The transformer is able to take care of the necessary polarity shift. As in the cathode-coupled multivibrator, the frequency of operation is determined to a great extent by the grid time constant (R1-C1).

In considering the operation of a blocking tube, assume that the grid is swinging in a positive direction from the conducting level.

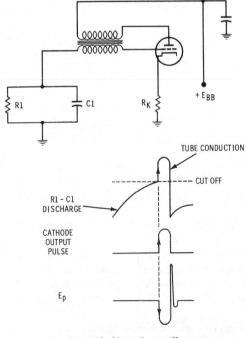

Fig. 2-32. Blocking-tube oscillator.

The plate current rises and the plate voltage falls. Through transformer action there is a further rise in grid voltage. Feedback drives the tube to a limiting level very quickly. At this point a further increase in grid voltage causes no further increase in plate current. Since there is no change in plate current, the transformer activity is stopped and the feedback voltage begins to fall off. The grid voltage now begins to fall and the feedback activity reverses direction. Now the tube is quickly driven to cutoff, as the built-up field about the transformer collapses. A resultant high negative voltage across the transformer secondary drives the grid far beyond cutoff.

The tube remains cut off until capacitor C1 has had time enough to discharge through resistor R1 to the conduction level of the tube. At this time a new cycle of events begins.

A positive pulse can be derived from the cathode circuit. The only time a positive voltage can appear across the cathode resistor occurs when the tube is conducting. This can only happen for the short interval of time during which the feedback activity takes place—when the grid voltage rises to the limiting level and then quickly drops into cutoff. As a result, a clean short-duration pulse is available at the cathode.

A negative pulse can be removed at the plate of the blocking circuit during the same time interval. However, when the transformer's field collapses after the grid voltage passes the cutoff level, a sharp high-voltage positive spike occurs at the trailing edge of the negative plate pulse. Often a blocking transformer includes a third winding. It is possible to obtain a high-amplitude steep short-duration pulse from across this winding.

Synchronization—The MV and BO oscillators just described are called free-running, or astable, types because switching from one tube to the other occurs automatically, and there is no need for an external trigger or control voltage. If circuit components are chosen well and a good design is used, MV and BO oscillators can be used as stable timing oscillators for radar sets. They generate a sharp trigger pulse directly in this application, and no sine-wave oscillator and follow-up shaping circuits are used.

Relaxation oscillators of this type can also be locked-in or synchronized by trigger pulses. They then are made to operate on the same frequency, and in phase with, the sync trigger. Such oscillators can be a part of the sweep generating system of a radar set which forms the deflection sawtooth waves for the radar display tube. In this application they are synchronized by the timing trigger or gate pulses.

A blocking oscillator (Fig. 2-33), for example, can be synchronized by a positive trigger applied to its grid. The blocking oscillator normally is designed to operate on a free-running frequency a bit higher than the intended trigger signal. As shown, the positive trigger spike reaches up to drive the tube into conduction just ahead of the start-of-conduction time for its free-running period. It is important to recognize then that each conduction period is initiated by the trigger in the same way, and, therefore, the oscillator frequency becomes that of the trigger repetition rate instead of the free-running frequency. Since each trigger initiates the conduction time of the tube, the leading edge of the

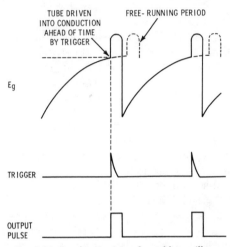

Fig. 2-33. Synchronization of astable oscillator.

cathode pulse coincides with the incoming trigger. Thus it can be stated that the oscillator output pulse is locked, in both phase and frequency, to the trigger pulse.

A cathode-coupled multivibrator can be synchronized in a similar manner by a positive sync pulse applied to its RC-coupled grid. A conventional multivibrator can be synchronized by a positive trigger on either grid. More often a negative trigger is applied to one of the plates and is then amplified by the conducting section of the tube. It then appears as an amplified positive trigger on the grid of the nonconducting tube, driving it into conduction.

Monostable and Bistable Operation—Multivibrators and blocking circuits can be arranged in circuits that are not free running. There are two major categories for multivibrators: monostable and bistable. A blocking tube can be operated in the monostable class but not as a bistable. For both types of operation the relaxation circuits remain in a stable state until they are acted on by an arriving trigger. If there are no arriving trigger pulses, they do not oscillate.

In the case of the monostable type, the trigger initiates the removal of the circuit from its stable state for a specific time interval, after which it returns automatically to its stable condition and awaits the arrival of the next trigger. In a bistable type there are two stable states, and the arriving triggers simply switch or flip-flop between the two conditions.

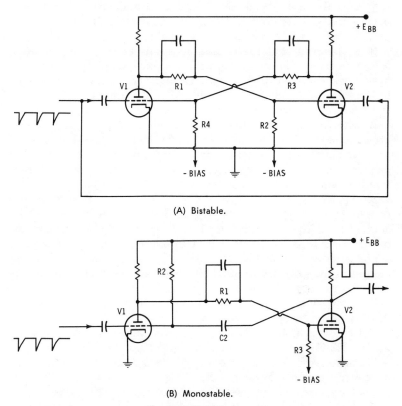

(A) Bistable.

(B) Monostable.

Fig. 2-34. Multivibrators.

The bistable multivibrator of Fig. 2-34A depends on a negative grid bias to maintain its two stable states. When it is first turned on, there is some unbalance, and feedback causes one tube to conduct, and drives the other to cutoff.

If we assume V1 is conducting and V2 is cut off, it is the R1-R2 bleeder network which holds V2 cut off. The plate voltage is low because of conducting V1, and the negative bias dominates.

A negative trigger at the grid of V1 appears positive at V1 plate and on the grid of V2. It drives V2 into conduction and initiates the feedback activity that drives V1 to cutoff. V1 holds at cutoff, because of the R3-R4 bleeder and the low V2 plate voltage when V1 is conducting.

This is the second stable state of the multivibrator. Now V2 is conducting and V1 is cut off. The circuit will remain stable until the next trigger. The negative trigger at the grid of V2 appears as a positive trigger at the grid of V1. Here it raises the grid-cathode voltage of V1 to conduction level and initiates the feedback activity that turns on V1 and shuts off V2. The second trigger, therefore, has returned the multivibrator to its first state.

It is apparent that the operational activity is much the same as that of a free-running type, with one exception. Operation does not switch between tubes automatically; rather, the MV remains in a stable state and switches only under the influence of arriving triggers. With no triggers, there is no switching.

A monostable multivibrator is shown in Fig. 2-34B. In this arrangement V1 is conducting in the stable state because its grid-cathode voltage is held near zero by returning its high-value grid resistor R2 to the supply voltage. The combination of negative bias and the R1-R3 bleeder keep V2 below cutoff.

A negative trigger applied at the grid of V1 is passed by the conducting section (V1) and appears as a positive trigger on the grid of V2. The resultant feedback, as in previous examples, drives V2 into conduction and V1 into cutoff. The cutoff time of V1 depends on the time constant R2-C2. Because no cutoff biasing is used in the grid circuit of V2, it will again conduct after C2 has been discharged. Feedback now brings the MV back to its single stable state with V1 conducting and V2 cut off. Here it will hold until the next trigger arrives.

The interval that the MV is in its nonstable condition depends on the R2-C2 time constant. During the conducting interval of V2, a negative pulse can be removed from its plate. The duration of the pulse depends on the R2-C2 grid time constant; its frequency depends on the rate of arrival of the trigger pulses.

A blocking circuit can be operated in a monostable manner by returning its grid resistor to a cutoff bias voltage, as in Fig. 2-35. An applied positive trigger then drives the grid to conduction level. As in a free-running blocking oscillator, the feedback drives the grid to the limiting point, and then sharply beyond cutoff. However, in the monostable case, because of the cutoff bias voltage the conduction level is not reached even after C1 has discharged completely through R1. No feedback activity will begin until the next positive trigger arrives.

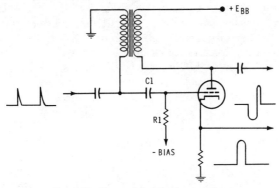

Fig. 2-35. Monostable blocking oscillator.

Pulses can be removed from the cathode or plate circuits. Their duration depends on blocking circuit constants; their frequency depends on the arriving trigger pulses.

2-3-4. Relaxation Master Oscillators

An example of a gas-tube timing-pulse generator that can be used in a small radar set is shown in Fig. 2-36. The grid of the thyratron is so biased with resistors R1 and R2 that without any appreciable charge on capacitor C1, the thyratron will conduct. As soon as the tube conducts and the gas ionizes, it presents a very low resistance path to the supply voltage (E_{BB}). Capacitor C1 immediately charges to the supply voltage level. Since resistor R3 is of such a low value, the capacitor charges in 1 or 2 microseconds, because the time constant of the combination is extremely short.

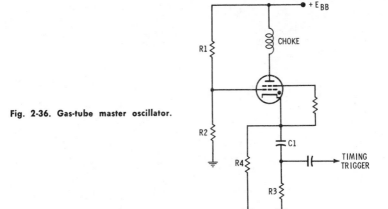

Fig. 2-36. Gas-tube master oscillator.

The charge on the capacitor is such that the gas tube is de-ionized and ceases conduction. It will not conduct again until capacitor C1 discharges through resistor R4. The discharge time is of course very long because of the high value of resistor R4. For example, it may be hundreds of microseconds before the charge on C1 drops to a low enough value that the gas tube will once again ionize. Eventually the capacitor does discharge to the level at which the gas tube can again conduct and ionize. At this point the cycle is repeated.

It is apparent that by controlling the time constant of C1-R3 the conduction time can be regulated. Thus a very short-duration and high-amplitude pulse will be developed across resistor R3. The discharge time of the combination (C1-R4) determines the spacing between pulses and therefore the actual frequency or repetition rate of the generated pulses.

Inasmuch as the output is derived when the gas tube conducts, a positive trigger pulse, the amplitude of which approaches the supply voltage, is made available across resistor R3. This can serve as the basic timing pulse for the radar system. All other circuits are synchronized by this trigger.

A blocking-tube timing oscillator for a small-boat radar set is shown in Fig. 2-37. It is a free-running type that is stabilized by returning the grid circuit to a positive voltage point. This improves the stability of the blocking tube by making the active part of the grid time-constant discharge cycle more linear. If the grid capacitor, as shown in the waveforms, is discharged to zero

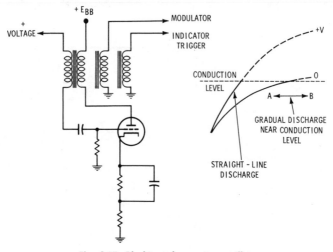

Fig. 2-37. Blocking-tube master oscillator.

level, the discharge curve is more exponential between maximum negative charge and the conducting level of the tube. Thus, the discharge is "near" conduction level for a considerable period of time (A to B) and minor disturbances can delay or start conduction prematurely on a rather irregular basis, affecting frequency and phase stability.

The discharge is in a more straight-line manner when the grid circuit is returned to a plus voltage. Therefore circuit variations have less influence on the time interval between maximum negative charge of the grid capacitor and the conduction level of the blocking tube.

Notice that the transformer has two windings in addition to the primary and secondary. The pulse voltage derived from one of the windings is a sharp spike which is used as a trigger pulse for the modulator section of the radar set. A second trigger pulse is derived from the fourth winding to synchronize the indicator and various other radar circuits.

2-3-5. Modulator

The first stage of the modulator is usually a blocking tube or multivibrator. It operates under control of the timing trigger. Its output, in turn, is used to trigger a thyratron switch. This switch releases energy, stored in a network, as a high-powered pulse that turns on the magnetron oscillator.

In the modulator it is necessary to generate a pulse of a precise duration without any adjustments. There are, of course, various methods of generating a pulse of specific duration. Two such methods, as covered previously, involve either differentiation or proper time constants associated with a multivibrator or blocking pulse generator. However, in generating a power pulse, quite a different approach must be used if a steep-sided pulse is to be formed with a close tolerance. The method of Fig. 2-38 is common to most radar modulators.

A thyratron with its high-current capability and low resistance serves as a fast-acting power switch. An associated delay line provides the duration stability and steep-sided pulse required. The source of energy for the modulator pulse is the high-voltage (HV) power supply. This can be a regular power-transformer and full-wave rectifier with an associated LC filter. In some of the small radar sets an oscillating high-voltage supply is used. The function of the high-voltage supply is to deliver energy for storage, through a charging choke and diode, to a pulse-forming network.

As shown in the charge-equivalent circuit (Fig. 2-39A), the charging choke and the distributed capacitance of the circuit

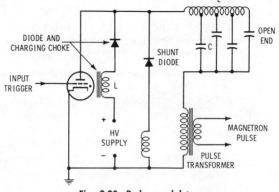

Fig. 2-38. Radar modulator.

(largely the capacitance of the pulse-forming network) form a series resonant circuit. When the thyratron switch opens after a transmit pulse, energy flows out of the power supply and shock-excites the resonant circuit into oscillation. In so doing, as per the waveform of Fig. 2-39, the resonant capacitor charges to twice the supply voltage. This charge to twice the supply voltage is accomplished by setting the resonant circuit on a frequency that is one half the pulse repetition rate. Consequently, at the approxi-

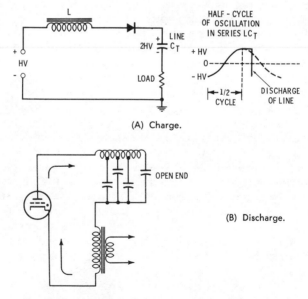

Fig. 2-39. Charge and discharge equivalent of a thyratron.

mate time of full capacitor charge the next trigger pulse arrives at the thyratron, and the energy is released from the delay line. Ordinarily, the resonant frequency and the pulse repetition rate would have to be matched rather exactly to derive maximum pulse power. However, a charging diode is associated with the network. This diode becomes nonconducting when the capacitor is fully charged, permitting the delay line to hold a charge for a longer interval of time.

The use of a charging choke improves the efficiency of operation because there is little energy absorbed by the choke as compared to the losses that would occur were a resistor used instead. Likewise, the charging choke prevents the delay line from discharging any significant energy into the HV power source when the thyratron switch is fired.

The delay line has the characteristic of a transmission line even though it is made of lumped constants. The artificial line is composed of either a tapped inductor or a series of individual inductors. Individual capacitors are connected to ground from the taps or coil junctions.

The duration of the pulse and the characteristic impedance of the artificial line are determined by the L and C values. A characteristic impedance is used that can be matched to the input impedance of the pulse transformer. A proper match makes certain that maximum power is delivered to the pulse transformer input. The pulse transformer, in turn, has the necessary turns ratio to match the primary impedance to the input impedance of the magnetron oscillator. In a typical case the characteristic impedance of the line would be 50 ohms and would match the 50-ohm input impedance of the pulse transformer. The turns ratio of the transformer is such that the 500- to 1000-ohm input impedance of the magnetron is reflected as a 50-ohm load to the primary side.

The shunt diode is used to drain off any residual voltage that remains on the line after the transmit pulse. By so doing, an abnormal charge does not build up on the line, and the amplitude of the discharge pulse remains constant.

Let us next consider the discharge activity (Fig. 2-39B) that occurs during the transmit time. A trigger pulse arrives at the thyratron and causes it to ionize and act as a closed switch. As soon as the switch is closed, half of the charge voltage across the pulse line appears across the primary of the pulse transformer, provided the primary impedance of the transformer is matched to the characteristic impedance of the line. The transfer is instantaneous with the firing of the thyratron, producing a steep leading edge.

When the voltage at the output side of the line is halved, energy travels in two directions: in part to the load and in part as a traveling wave that moves along the line to its open end. The energy moving along the line is reflected almost entirely from the open end and now moves in the opposite direction toward the load. In so doing, energy is continuously discharged into the load. This energy coming back from the open end sees a proper termination, all of the returning energy being eventually discharged into the load. The discharge occurs for the length of time required by the energy to travel down to the open end and back. When the last bit of energy goes into the load, the voltage at the end of the line drops abruptly, forming the steep trailing edge of the pulse.

During the discharge period, energy is sent into the load uniformly for a duration that corresponds to the time required for a wave to travel to the open end of the line and return. This delay time of the artificial line determines the exact duration of the pulse. The magnitude of the pulse is half the amplitude of the full charge voltage on the line. Therefore, in a resonant charging system the amplitude of the pulse approximates the voltage of the high-voltage source.

When the voltage drops in the discharge circuit, the thyratron current flow and anode voltage also drop. Therefore the thyratron switch deionizes and opens. This initiates a new line-charging activity. The energy stored in the line remains there until the next pulse triggers the thyratron.

2-4. INDICATOR CIRCUITS

Several synchronized activities occur in the indicator circuits, as mentioned previously in the functional block diagram discussion of Chapter 1. Sweep and range mark signals must be generated, and the video signal must be amplified and processed prior to its application to the radar display tube. An unblanking signal must be generated to turn on the scanning beam during trace intervals.

2-4-1. Gate Multivibrator

The gated multivibrator, under control of the timing trigger, generates the gate pulse that initiates various operations in the indicator circuit. Usually it is a monostable multivibrator, as shown in Fig. 2-40. In stable state V1 is cut off and V2 conducts. Note that a negative voltage is being applied to the grid of V1 to hold it at cutoff. A negative trigger is being supplied to the plate of V1. It is amplified by conducting section V2 and appears

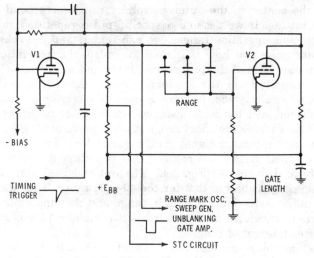

Fig. 2-40. Indicator-gate multivibrator.

as a positive trigger at the grid of V1, thus driving it into conduction. V1 plate voltage swings negative, driving the grid of V2 negative and plate of V2 positive. Regenerative feedback then drives V2 to cutoff. The duration of the cutoff time depends on the RC time constant in the grid circuit of V2. After the RC combination has discharged to the conducting level, feedback in opposite polarity restores the multivibrator to its steady state. Here it remains until the next trigger arrives.

In the indicator circuits all activities must be locked to the pulse repetition rate and the range timing. The former is established by the arriving trigger pulses, their repetition rate having been established previously by the timing oscillator. Range timing is established in the gated multivibrator by the switched capacitors and potentiometer in the grid circuit of V2.

A negative pulse corresponding to the cutoff interval of V2 can be removed at the plate of V1. This pulse is used to gate (turn on and off) the various indicator circuits. The gate pulses are important to the generation of the range rings, the generation of the sweep waveform, and the unblanking or gating-on of the scanning beam during trace intervals.

2-4-2. Sweep Generation

The sawtooth of current that passes through the deflection coil and moves the scanning beam from the center of the screen to the outer periphery must have the same frequency as the pulse repetition rate. Furthermore, the length of time required to move from the center to the outer periphery must correspond to the range setting. If we assume a specific pulse repetition rate and two possible operating ranges, we can understand the reason for the gate pulse and how it is able to control the generation of a sweep waveform of the proper amplitude and duration.

The amplitude of the sawtooth sweep current, regardless of range, must always be the same because the scanning beam must be deflected over the same distance—from center to outer periphery. However, for the short range it must move at a faster velocity, because the radar signal itself requires less time to propagate out to a near target and return. This condition is shown in the waveform drawings of Fig. 2-41. The out and back time for the 20-mile range is half of that for the 40-mile range. Thus the beam must move faster for the 20-mile range and the amplitude of the deflection waveform must rise from its minimum to maximum in a shorter interval of time.

Next consider how this sweep waveform can be regulated in a typical radar sweep circuit (Fig. 2-42). First of all, realize that the gate multivibrator helps with the duration problem. By switching the time constants in the grid circuit of V2, we can

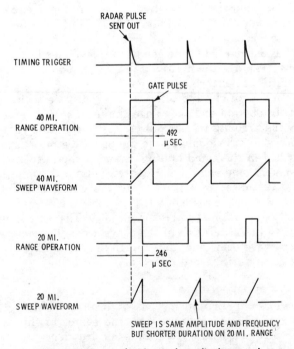

Fig. 2-41. Sweep duration and amplitude control.

form an output pulse that corresponds in duration to the travel time for a given maximum range. In other words, the duration of the gate pulse at the output of the multivibrator is twice as long for the 40-mile range as it is for the 20-mile range.

This gate signal is used to control the duration of the trace portion of the deflection waveform. A negative gate pulse is applied to the grid of the sweep generator. It drives the triode to cutoff, and the plate-circuit capacitor (C1) charges toward the supply voltage through resistors R1 and R2. The charge is

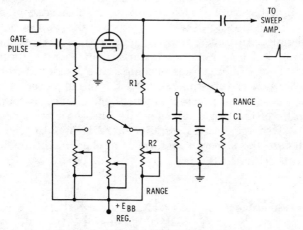

Fig. 2-42. Generation of sweep waveform.

over the essentially linear portion of the exponential charging cycle of the capacitor. The charge only continues until the trailing edge of the gate pulse causes the tube to go into conduction again. With the tube conducting, the charge placed on the capacitor is quickly drained off. The circuit then remains stable with the tube conducting until the next gate pulse comes along.

It is important to realize that the time of capacitor charge depends on the duration of the gate pulse. Thus, the trace portion of the sweep sawtooth coincides with the duration of the gate pulse and the maximum round-trip travel time for the particular range setting (Fig. 2-41).

If the range switch is set for shorter range operation, the duration of the gate pulse will be shorter. This means that the charge time of the capacitor is shorter, and if a different RC combination were not used in the plate circuit of the sweep generator, the sawtooth wave would not build up to the required amplitude. However, in switching the range, a smaller capacitor and lower-value resistor are switched into the plate circuit. The charging circuit now has a shorter time constant, and therefore the charge on the capacitor builds up faster. The component values are chosen so that on each range the amplitude to which the capacitor charges is the same, regardless of its duration of charge. As a result, the trace line as it appears on the radar screen will be of the same length regardless of the range position used. Suitable controls or preset adjustments are included so that the trace length can be set precisely on the radar screen.

One other factor must be considered when it is necessary to cause a sawtooth of current to flow in the deflection coil. If the deflection coil were a perfect inductor, a linear rise of current through the coil would take place with the application of a squared pulse. However, there is inherently some resistance in the circuit, and to maintain a linear rise of current, there must also be a linear rise in voltage to compensate for circuit resistance. As in television picture-tube circuits, the initial sweep waveform must be trapezoidal, a combination of pulse and sawtooth. The actual ratio of the two components depends on circuit constants. In some sweep-generating circuits there is a pulse component added before the sweep waveform is applied to the final sweep output tube (Fig. 2-43).

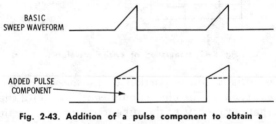

Fig. 2-43. Addition of a pulse component to obtain a linear deflection current.

The final deflection stage is a sweep power amplifier, often a beam-power tube. The voltage from the sweep generator is applied to its grid circuit. Its amplitude is such that a very high amplitude voltage is developed in the plate circuit. It is this squared voltage that causes the linear rise in current in the deflection coil. Slip-rings are used to feed the current into the rotating deflection coil.

2-4-3. Unblanking Gate

To prevent spurious patterns from appearing on the radar screen, the electron beam is turned on only during the active trace interval when the radar is sensitive to return echoes for the set range. This time interval must coincide with the gate pulse and the trace portion of the sweep waveform. An unblanking gate can be developed by amplifying the gate pulse and applying it with correct polarity to the grid-cathode circuit of the radar tube. In the example of Fig. 2-44 the negative gate pulse is amplified, flipped in polarity, and then applied to the control grid of the electron gun. Its polarity is such that during the gate interval the electron beam is turned on and directed toward the radar screen. Between gate pulses the grid is driven below cutoff be-

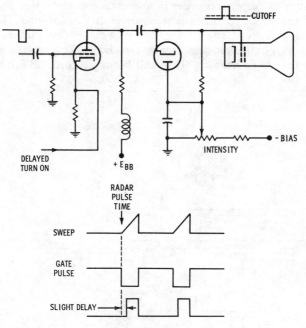

Fig. 2-44. Unblanking system.

cause of the negative base-line amplitude of the pulse. Thus the electron beam is cut off, except during the trace period for the specific operating range. Of course, the longer the range setting, the longer the time period the electron beam is turned on.

A diode clamp tube is used to maintain a fixed brightness level with changes in range setting. When the range setting is changed, the relative positive and negative portions of the gate waveform will vary. Since the signal averages about a zero axis, the voltage level during unblanking will shift, and the beam current will change. However, if the negative portion of the waveform is clamped at a fixed reference voltage, the pulse level that represents beam turn-on will always be the same, and the beam current and trace brightness will not change with different range settings.

Unblanking is often delayed slightly so that unblanking always starts at the screen center. The delay minimizes the influence of changing current averages in the deflection coil.

2-4-4. Servo System

The responsibility of the servo system is to rotate the antenna and the PPI trace in synchronism. In the arrangement of Fig. 2-45 a number of servo components are used to rotate the deflection coil of the PPI tube in synchronism with the antenna. Both the antenna and the deflection coils are rotated by motors. Their activity can be locked together in two ways. The reference angle can be the ship's heading. This will be angle zero; all other bear-

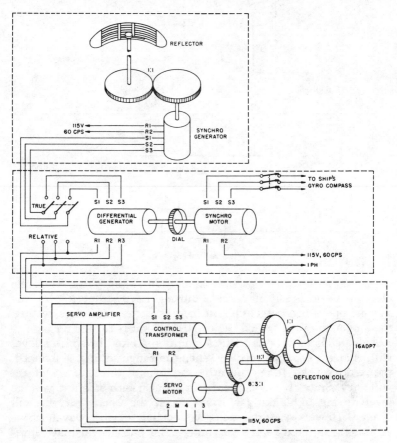

Fig. 2-45. Radar servo system.

ings will be taken with reference to the heading. In a second arrangement the zero reference angle can be true north. In this case, the entire radar display will rotate as the ship changes its course. The zero angle will always be true north regardless of the heading of the boat.

A synchro generator is mechanically coupled to the antenna rotation system. In a synchro generator a changing voltage is developed across the stator windings that corresponds to the position of the rotor shaft. A source of voltage must be connected to the rotor to serve as a reference voltage. This voltage then induces components into the stator coils as the rotor moves in synchronism with the antenna.

When the bearing is to be taken with regard to the ship's heading, the switch is set to the relative position. By so doing, the changing voltage at the output of the synchro generator is applied to a control transformer. A control transformer is also a rotating device, but it produces an output, usually called an "error signal." The error signal corresponds to the position of the rotor relative to the phasing of the applied stator signal, which is indicative of the rotor position of the synchro generator. When the two rotors are moving in synchronism, the output of the control transformer is zero. If they are out of sync, the phase differential and direction are represented by the error signal.

The above error signal is low in amplitude, and it is built up by a so-called servoamplifier. This amplifier develops the appropriate stator signals for the servomotor. In a servomotor the rotor moves in accordance with the voltages applied to its three stator windings.

The rotor of the servomotor is geared to the rotational system of the deflection coil. It speeds up or slows down the coil rotation until the error signal at the output of the control transformer drops to zero. Note that the rotor of the control transformer is geared to the rotational system of the deflection coil. Thus any corrections made by the servomotor will also be mechanically transmitted to the rotor of the control transformer.

When the radar bearing is to be referenced to true north, the servo system must be linked to the ship's gyro compass. A voltage corresponding to gyro position is applied to the stators of a synchro motor. The rotor moves in accordance with the stator voltages. Thus the position of the rotor becomes indicative of the ship's heading relative to true north. This movement is conveyed mechanically to the rotor of a differential generator.

For a true bearing calibration, the switch must be set to the true position. In so doing the stator voltages from the synchro generator (indicative of the rotation of the antenna) are applied to the stators of the differential generator. The differential generator develops a rotor output that is a function of stator voltages and rotor position. Thus a correction has been made in the voltage derived from the synchro generator that takes into consideration the information introduced with regard to the gyro compass bearing. This combined information now acts in the control transformer. In so doing, an error signal is developed that responds to any loss in synchronism between deflection-coil rotation and antenna-coil rotation and, at the same time, relates the antenna bearing to true north.

2-4-5. Range Ring Generation

The range-mark rings on the radar screen are formed by a series of sharp pulses or "pips." These pips have a period that matches the travel time for the particular distance range they calibrate. During each trace time (Fig. 2-46) these range-mark signals are applied to the grid-cathode circuit of the radar tube. Each one causes a brightening of the line when the trace is a specific distance from the center of the screen. All of these bright spots join together in a circle as the trace revolves because there is a new pip for each sweep line as it swings out from the center of the screen. This circle then represents a specific mileage distance.

How is it possible to generate a range-mark signal that corresponds to a specific round-trip travel time? In earlier discussions you learned that the round trip time can be measured in microseconds. For example, a round trip to the 5-mile range corresponds to 61.8 microseconds (5 × 12.36). This would tell us, in the case of a 20-mile range setting, that a pip should be generated when the trace line is one-quarter distance to the outer periphery of the radar screen. Let's go a step further and assume that range rings are also to be placed at 10-, 15-, and 20-mile distances. Note that these are separated by a distance of 5 miles and correspond again to additional increments of 5 miles, or 61.8 microseconds.

From the preceding we can deduce that if a series of four pips is generated for each trace, these pips would have to be equidistantly spaced in time and would occur when the trace is one quarter, one half, three quarter, and full distance to the outer periphery. Most important, these indicate that if we generate a signal with a period that corresponds to the 5-mile round-trip distance, they will set off range rings that correspond to 5, 10, 15, and 20 miles.

In a range-mark generator this is accomplished by using resonant circuits. The particular resonant circuit associated with a desired mileage calibration is shock-excited into oscillation by

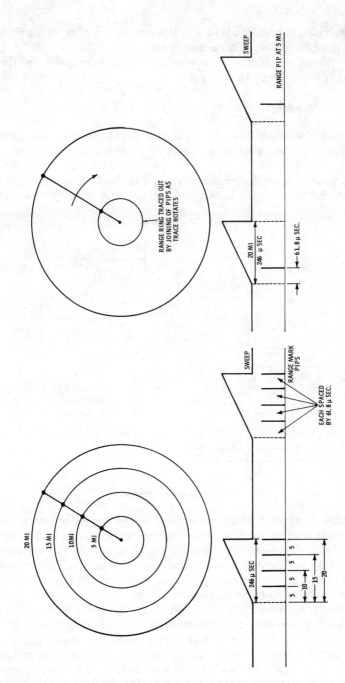

Fig. 2-46. Range-mark signals and scope rings.

the gate pulse. Thus we also tie in the generation of the pips with the start of the trace as is necessary.

If 5-mile range rings are to be generated, the frequency of the sine wave must be 16.18 kilocycles:

$$f = \frac{1}{\text{period}} = \frac{1}{61.8\,\mu\,\text{sec}} = 16.18\,\text{kc}$$

Note that the separation between the peaks of the generated sine waves corresponds to a round-trip time out to the 5-mile range.

A range-mark oscillator is shown in Fig. 2-47. The input tube (VI) of the range-mark oscillator is conducting heavily when no

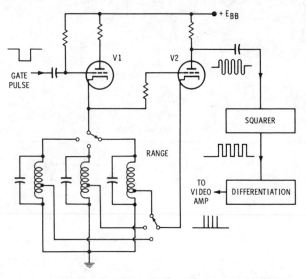

Fig. 2-47. Range-mark generator.

gate pulse is applied. With the arrival of the negative gate pulse the tube is shut off quickly. Inasmuch as there results a substantial current change in the cathode resonant circuit, it is shock-excited into oscillation. In effect, the resonant tank circuit stands isolated, and all of the energy in the tank circuit must be dissipated in the form of oscillations.

Normally such oscillations would be in the form of a damped wave, each wave decreasing in amplitude until all of the energy is dissipated. However, a feedback path holds the oscillations at a constant amplitude. Note that the tank circuit is coupled to the grid of the second tube and that the cathode of this tube is connected back into the resonant circuit. The feedback link holds the amplitude of the sine wave constant for the duration of the input gate pulse. At the conclusion of the gate pulse the first tube again goes into heavy conduction and the oscillations cease. Thus the output of the range-mark oscillator is a burst of sine waves lasting for the duration of the gate pulse. Since the gate pulse matches the duration of the radar sweep, the range mark signals are only generated during the active trace time.

The bursts of sine waves are next applied to a limiter clipper. Here the sine waves are shaped into square waves with fast leading and trailing edges, but an unchanged frequency.

The output of the squarer is applied to an RC differentiating network. As covered previously, a differentiator emphasizes the edges of the square wave; thus, positive and negative spikes are developed at the output. The spacings between adjacent positive and adjacent negative spikes still correspond to 61.8 microseconds (16.18-kilocycle period).

The purpose of the next stage is to remove either the positive or negative spikes, depending on which ones are to be used in the system. These spikes will then be inserted with proper polarity into the video amplifier of the indicator.

It is to be noted from Fig. 2-46 that the time separation between adjacent spikes corresponds to a round-trip time of 5 miles. Thus with relation to the gate pulse the first spike would be separated from the leading edge of the gate pulse and the start of the radar trace by 61.8 microseconds. The second negative spike is separated by an additional 61.8 microseconds. Now the total separation from the leading edge of the gate pulse and the start of the complete trace is 123.6 microseconds. This corresponds to a round trip time out to a 10-mile range. Thus the second pip will place itself on the radar screen as a 10-mile calibration point.

The third and fourth pips correspond to round-trip times from 15- and 20-mile distances. Thus the four pips, separated by 5-mile timing, trace the 5-, 10-, 15-, and 20-mile range rings on the screen.

2-4-6. The Video Amplifier

The responsibility of the indicator video amplifier is to amplify the target signals demodulated at the video detector to the proper level for controlling (intensity-modulating) the electron beam of the radar scope. The range-mark signals are also added at an appropriate point in the video amplifier and are applied jointly with the video signal to the grid-cathode circuit of the radar tube. Two or more stages of amplification are employed.

In the example of Fig. 2-48, both the range pips and the video signal are applied to the input of the video amplifier. The two signal sources are isolated from each other with a resistor and diode network. The diode presents a high impedance path to any signal attempting to travel in the opposite direction. Thus, the desired signals pass with minimum attentuation to the grid of the first video amplifier, and at the same time cross modulation into the two signal sources is blocked.

In the example, the range-mark pips and return-echo signals are going into the first grid with negative polarity. They appear positive-going both at the plate and on the grid of the next video

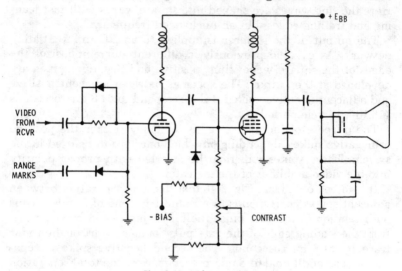

Fig. 2-48. Video amplifier.

stage. Note that peaking coils are used in the plate circuits much as in the video amplifier of a television receiver. In so doing, the sharp pulses are not stretched out (integrated), but reproduced with all their inherent sharpness at the cathode of the radar tube. This is important in obtaining a sharp radar display and a clean-cut separation between targets.

The output stage is a combination of power and voltage amplifier that builds up the video signal to the high amplitude needed to excite the cathode-grid circuit of the radar tube. The radar signals appear negative-going at the cathode of the radar tube. Therefore they increase the intensity of the beam whenever they appear and make a corresponding bright mark on the radar screen.

A DC restorer diode is present in the input circuit of the radar scope. This clamps the base line to a fixed voltage level. Hence there will be no change in the average illumination of the screen as a result of changes in the average signal content. The system will remain peak-responding, reproducing signals in terms of a brightness intensity that correspond to the actual peak level of the return echo. Likewise, the range rings will be reproduced with a constant brightness regardless of incoming signal variations.

The contrast control that regulates the peak level of the video signal is located in the grid circuit of the video output tube. It regulates the negative grid bias and sets the gain of the video output stage.

2-4-7. Radar Tube Circuit

A typical radar tube schematic is shown in Fig. 2-49. All of the radar activity converges on this point. Typical waveforms are shown to indicate relative relationships that have been established previously by proper timing activity. In the presentation it has been assumed that a target signal is being received at the 12.5-mile range with the radar set to its 20-mile operating range.

The electron gun, as in conventional CRT practice, consists of cathode, control grid, accelerating grid, focusing electrode, and anode. The particular tube of Fig. 2-49 uses electrostatic focusing and magnetic deflection. Centering can be accomplished with magnets or external centering coils, depending on tube design. An external rotating deflection coil is used to generate the active radar trace.

Various types of high-voltage supplies are used, such as oscillating and fly-back types. In the example, a separate power transformer and silicon rectifier voltage-quadrupler are used to form the high anode voltage. Simple RC filters are used to take out the ripple. A voltage multiplier of this type can be used with good regulation because of the low current demand of the CRT.

Take a look at the various signals that must be applied to the radar tube. A sawtooth of current must be applied in the deflection coil. The linear rise in current occurs during the active trace period or listening time of the radar set for a given range setting. During this trace interval the electron beam must be active and visible. It is turned on in the example by a negative unblanking pulse applied to the cathode. This is the same as putting a positive unblanking pulse on the grid. If the electron beam is turned on and the deflection coil *is not rotated*, a visible but stationary trace line appears somewhere on the screen. With the deflection coil rotating in synchronism with the antenna the trace line is not only visible but revolves around the face of the screen.

In the example, range-mark signals are being applied as positive pips or spikes to the control grid. Therefore whenever they occur the screen is made more bright for a very short instant of time, causing bright dots to appear at equidistant points along the trace. In the example four such bright spots will appear. With the deflection coil in rotation these bright pips blend into four visible rings because the same activity repeats for each trace.

The video signal is also applied to the control grid. The transmit pulse and target signals swing positive. This illuminates the very center of the screen and also places a target blip on the screen when the antenna matches the target bearing. The target blip will fall at a position somewhere between the 10- and 15-mile range rings. Note that it appears in the composite video signal (be-

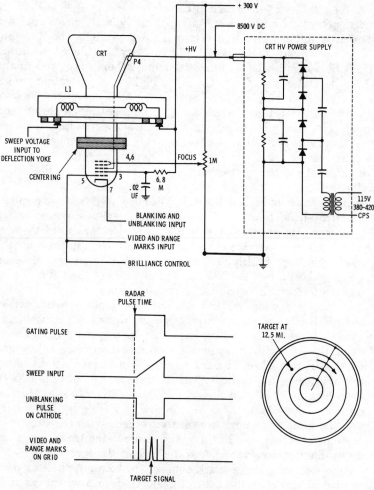

Fig. 2-49. Radar display tube.

tween the 10- and 15-mile range pips) which is applied to the grid of the radar tube.

The overall brightness of the screen can be controlled with an adjustable grid-cathode bias. The brilliance control sets the grid bias.

2-5.   RECEIVER

The receiver intercepts, amplifies, and demodulates the incoming target signals. It is a superheterodyne type and is similar in most respects to superheterodyne receivers in general. However, in terms of radar operation, there are several additional receiver functions.

2-5-1.   RF Head

In the duplexer section of the radar set there are two takeoff points for the receiver. As shown in Fig. 2-50, the crystal mixer is inserted directly into the wave-guide section. Two outputs are

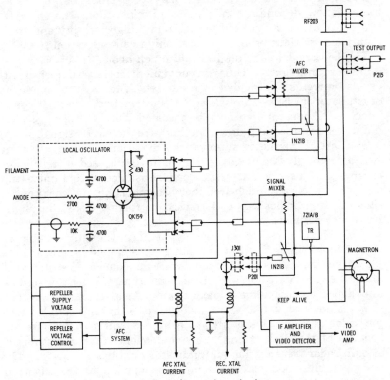

Fig. 2-50. Radar receiver circuits.

taken from the klystron local oscillator for use as injection signals. In the receive-crystal mixer the incoming signal and the local oscillator signal mix to produce an IF signal component. The local oscillator is tuned higher or lower than the signal frequency by the amount of the IF frequency. IF frequencies range in value from 30 to 120 megacycles. In the AFC crystal mixer a weak component of the transmit pulse and the local-oscillator signal mix to produce an IF component.

As mentioned previously, in some radar sets the receiver IF stages are divided between the RF head and the main part of the radar set. In other installations the complete IF amplifier and AM detector are mounted on a single chassis. The signal-to-noise ratio is determined largely by the input IF stage. Hence it is important to mount it as near as possible to the crystal mixer. Low-noise pentode or triode cascode circuits are used in the input stages. These amplifiers build up the signal, with a minimum contribution of noise, prior to those stages that give high-gain amplification.

The total number of IF stages may vary from four up to as many as ten, depending on design and application. The early IF stages are often neutralized to maintain a high stability and freedom from spurious oscillations with high-gain operation.

The DC crystal currents indicate much about the operation of duplexer and mixer. Thus, a convenient means of measuring crystal currents is provided in radar sets. The DC component of crystal current flows through an LC filter network to a jack into which a DC current meter can be inserted. The LC filter prevents the meter from loading down the high-frequency IF signal.

The last IF amplifier supplies the modulated IF signal 'o an AM detector. This detector is similar to those used in television receivers. It uses a low-value load resistance to minimize the attenuation of any high-frequency components in the return signals. Often a peaking coil is used to further boost the high-frequency response.

If the signal must be sent over a significant length of cable to the video amplifier input of the indicator, a cathode follower output stage can be used. Its high input impedance does not load down the video detector, and at the same time, it has a low output impedance for matching a coaxial cable. As a result, the desired signal is not attenuated, and spurious signals are not coupled into the video section. This is always a hazard within radar circuits because of the very strong pulse components that are inherent in both radar transmission and indicator circuits.

Proper electrode potentials must be applied to the klystron local oscillator. For best stability the voltages are often regulated.

Klystron local-oscillator frequency can be changed either by varying the dimensions of klystron cavity, or by adjusting the DC component of the repeller voltage. A manual adjustment of the DC repeller voltage can be used to vary the repeller voltage and make a fine adjustment of the local-oscillator frequency. The AFC system of the radar receiver also supplies an error DC voltage to the repeller plate to make the necessary corrections in the local-oscillator frequency for optimum operation of the crystal mixer.

2-5-2. Sensitivity Time Control (STC)

Two problems in the operation of a radar receiver are the strength of the transmit pulse component (main bang) in the IF amplifier, and the relatively greater strength of nearby target

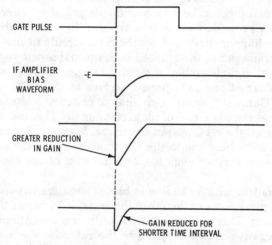

Fig. 2-51. Typical STC control waveform.

signals. One such strong-signal return is referred to as "sea return," or clutter, and it is a result of reflections from the water within a short distance of the radar set. The ill effects of these strong-signal components can be reduced by lowering the gain of the receiver during the initial part of the trace when there is the possibility of very strong target signals. This is done as shown in Fig. 2-51. A "shaped" bias waveform, coincident with the indicator gate pulse, causes the receiver gain to rise gradually from a low value to the preferred high-gain value needed for distant target reception. Thus the excessive "spreading brightness" and clutter on the display screen caused by nearby reflections is substantially reduced.

Often two controls are associated with the STC system. One control regulates the magnitude of the gain control, as demonstrated in the typical waveforms. It determines just how the receiver gain will be dropped during the initial part of the receive activity. In effect, it adjusts the sensitivity of the receiver to nearby targets. A second control is used to adjust the length of time during which STC action will occur. It sets the slope of the STC waveform, and therefore the distance range over which STC action will occur. The operator, by adjusting these controls, can minimize the ill effects of clutter, and at the same time the receiver can be made to display maximum sensitivity to distant target return. At the same time, it does not completely cancel out the return from nearby targets.

A typical STC-waveform generator is shown in Fig. 2-52. It is turned on by a positive pulse from the gate circuit of the indicator. Normally the tube is nonconducting, and no current flows through the grounded plate load resistor R_L. Hence there is no negative voltage contributed by the STC circuit to the bias line. The IF amplifiers are then biased with normal sensitivity to long-range target signals. When a positive trigger that is coincident with the start of the gate period arrives at the grid, the triode conducts. Current flow is such that a negative voltage will be developed at the plate end of plate resistor R_L. This places a negative charge on the STC output capacitor. Inasmuch as this charge is placed on the bias line to the IF amplifier stage, the stages will now be biased further negative, and the gain of the receiver will be less.

The extent to which the line is biased negative depends on the amount of plate current flow through resistor R_L when the trigger pulse arrives. This can be adjusted with the potentiometer that sets the negative voltage applied to the cathode. The more negative this voltage is made, the more negative will be the voltage placed on the bias line by tube conduction.

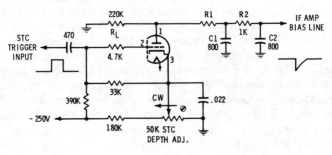

Fig. 2-52. STC circuit.

The rate at which the negative voltage decreases on the IF bias line depends on the time constant of bias-line filter resistors R1 and R2, and capacitors C1 and C2. The discharge of the capacitors is exponential, and therefore the gain of the IF amplifier changes in a like manner. Actually the receiver sensitivity increases with time and with distance to the target. After an interval of time, the negative voltage is completely discharged from the capacitors, and the receiver displays maximum sensitivity.

In some radar sets a like waveform is also used to control the sensitivity of the video amplifier of the indicator. This joint activity further reduces the brightness with which nearby targets are displayed on the screen. Furthermore, a strong negative pulse is often generated in synchronism with the transmit pulse. This strong pulse is applied directly to two or more IF amplifier stages, biasing them substantially negative during the transmit pulse. This reduces the intense brightness of the main bang pulse as it appears at the center of the screen. As a result the brightness does not spread out over a large area and it is possible to discern nearby targets more readily because they are not obscured by the main bang brightness.

2-5-3. AFC Systems

As mentioned previously, an AFC system is used to maintain the proper frequency difference between magnetron and klystron frequencies. When this is done, a returning target signal is always converted to an exact IF frequency. In many small-boat radar systems AFC is not employed. Modern magnetron and local-oscillator circuits have a higher stability, and with the proper IF bandwidth, AFC is not necessary for short to medium range.

A typical AFC circuit arrangement is shown in Fig. 2-53. The difference-pulse component is amplified in an IF amplifier and applied to an AFC discriminator. The AFC discriminator consists of two resonant sections with an identical Q; these sections are tuned to some precise frequency above and below the center frequency of the IF amplifier. Note that capacitors C1 and C2 are not of the same value. The two resonant circuits supply signals to separate diode detectors. If the frequency of the IF pulse is the exact frequency of the IF amplifier, the same magnitude of IF signal is applied to both diodes. When the detectors are balanced, they conduct exactly the same amount of current, and the net pulse output of the discriminator is zero.

When there is a drift in magnetron or local-oscillator frequency, the frequency of the IF pulse will shift above or below the IF center frequency. Therefore one diode will receive a stronger signal than the other. For example, if there is a 1-megacycle fre-

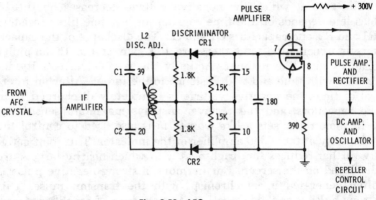

Fig. 2-53. AFC system.

quency drop, the response of the top tuned circuit is such that a stronger pulse component will be applied to the top diode than the lower diode. Therefore there will be a net positive pulse at the output of the discriminator. However, if the frequency drifts in the opposite direction, there will be a stronger negative pulse than positive pulse at the output of the discriminator.

In summary, the polarity of the pulse output of the discriminator depends on the direction of frequency drift. The magnitude of the pulse output will depend on the extent of the drift away from center frequency.

The pulse output of the discriminator can then be amplified and eventually rectified to produce a DC component of error voltage. Through a DC amplifier this DC component can be used to make a controlling adjustment on the repeller voltage. The desired difference frequency is re-established at the output of the AFC mixer. Of course, in doing so, the proper IF frequency also appears at the output of the receiver crystal mixer with the reception of a target signal.

One of the problems of controlling the frequency of the klystron local oscillator is that the drift can be so great as to be out of range of the AFC action. Hence it is customary to also use a sawtooth voltage generator in association with the DC amplifier that is operated by the AFC error voltage. For a substantial drift there will be no bias applied to the DC amplifier and it will operate as a sawtooth generator. It will sweep periodically over the necessary voltage range to bring the klystron local oscillator on the proper frequency. When the klystron frequency is swept within range of operation of the AFC system, a bias voltage reappears and shuts down the sawtooth generator activity. AFC hold will then be maintained in normal fashion.

CHAPTER 3

Small-Boat Radar Sets

Small and low-power radar sets have become increasingly popular for small pleasure and commercial boats. The entire radar set is composed of three or four compact units. The radar tube is usually a 7-inch type and the small-size indicator can be mounted at a position convenient to the pilot (Fig. 3-1).

Range of transmission is up to a maximum of 20 miles. Antenna systems are such that a narrow horizontal beam and a substantially wider vertical beam can be obtained. The PPI type of display is universal, with the antenna system rotating through 360°.

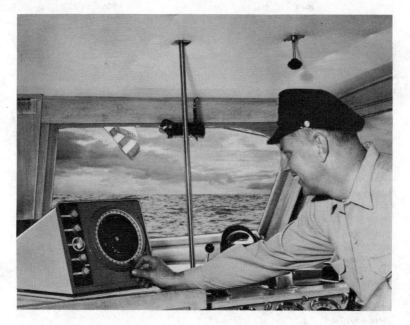

Courtesy Raytheon Co.

Fig. 3-1. Radar-antenna indicator aboard a yacht.

3-1. RAYTHEON PATHFINDER RADAR

The pathfinder is a three-unit radar consisting of an indicator, antenna assembly, and power supply. Operation is on 9410 mc with a peak transmit power of 3.5 kw. Pulse rate and length are 2000 pps and 0.14 microsecond respectively. The other specifications are given in Table 3-1.

Table 3-1. Radar Set Specifications

Frequency: 9410 megacycles ±50 mc.

Peak Transmitter Power: 3.5 Kw Nominal

Pulse Length: .14 Microsecond

Repetition Rate: 2000 Pulses per second ±5%

Receiver Noise: Less than 12 DB

Minimum Displayed Range: 30 Yards

Maximum Range: 12 Miles

Range Resolution: 30 yards at ½ mile range

Bearing Resolution: 55 yards at ½ mile range

Bearing Accuracy: Less than 1° error between actual bearing and indicated bearing.

Range Scales and Range Rings:

Scale	Ring
½ Mile	½ Mile
2 Mile	½ Mile
6 Mile	3 Mile
12 Mile	3 Mile

Range Ring Accuracy—5% or better

Antenna Power Beam
Horizontal: 3° @ —3DB Point
Vertical: 27° @ —3DB Point
Side Lobe Level: —21DB or better

ANTENNA: Two 30″ Folded Parabolic Antennas serve as transmitting and receiving antennas respectively. Magnetron is integral with transmitting antenna. L.O. Klystron and single-ended crystal mixer integral with receiving antenna.
Antenna Rotation: 20 R.P.M.

Magnetron: QK-798
Modulator: KU99
Klystron: 2K25

Single-Ended Crystal Mixer: 1N23B

INDICATOR:
PPI Tube: 7APB7
Focus: Electrostatic
Deflection: Magnetic
Deflection Coil Drive: Synchronous Direct Drive
Panel Controls: Power On-Off, Sync, Cursor, Range Selection, S.T.C.-Gain, F.T.C., Intensity, Tune
I.F. Bandwidth: 6 mc. at center frequency of 30 mc.
Video Bandwidth: 5 mc.

3-1-1. Block-Diagram Description

The two major units of the radar set are shown in block diagram form (Fig. 3-2). The receiver and transmitter are integral to the antenna system; they are mounted within the antenna radome (Fig. 3-3). The transmitter is mounted on the top deck, and it is an integral part of a transmit-pillbox antenna. The lower deck mounts the receiver, which is integral to the separate receive-pillbox antenna.

The separate receive and transmit antennas are almost duplicates of each other except for the method of feed, as shown in Fig. 3-4. Both antennas rotate simultaneously beneath the radome. The pillbox structure provides a high degree of isolation between the two antennas. Only a small amount of energy is interchanged between the transmit section and the receive section. Thus it is not necessary to employ a duplexer (no TR or ATR tubes). However, enough energy is exchanged between transmit and receive sections for tuning purposes.

Energy is launched into the transmit antenna via an antenna probe and a very short section of wave guide which directs the energy on to the reflecting parabolic segment of the pillbox antenna. For receive the incoming energy is reflected off the parabolic segment into a wave-guide termination that houses the receive crystal. The horizontal beam width of the antenna is 3°; vertical beam width is 27°. The bearing resolution is such that two targets separated by 55 yards at ½ mile can be delineated. The range resolution is 30 yards at the ½-mile range, indicating the capability of the radar set to evaluate a target that is a very short distance from the antenna system.

The master oscillator is shown at the lower right of the antenna system block diagram (Fig. 3-2). It is a gas-tube oscillator. Pulse-shaping and modulator blocks follow. A trigger pulse is also formed, and it is conveyed via a single multi-conductor cable that links the antenna assembly with the indicator.

The receive block diagram is shown at the left, beginning with the separate receive antenna and the follow-up crystal mixer. A 2K25 klystron is used as the local oscillator. The input section is followed by a five-stage IF amplifier. A crystal AM video detector and a cathode follower complete the receiver. The output from the cathode follower is conveyed through a cable to the indicator.

The video amplifier blocks are shown at the left side of the indicator diagram. The radar set includes an FTC- (fast time constant) switching arrangement which can be used to obtain more distinct separations between closely spaced targets on the

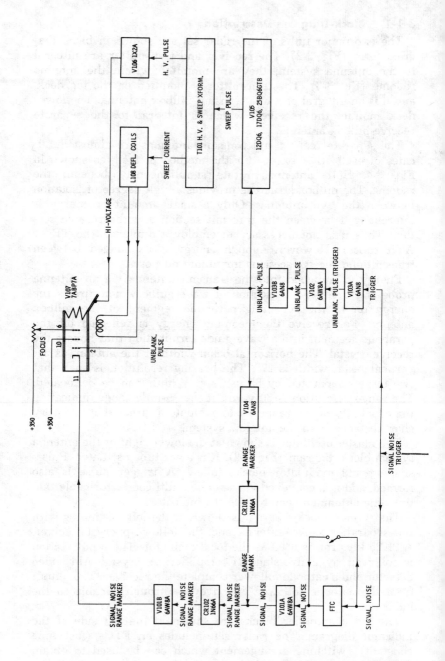

Fig. 3-2. Functional diagram

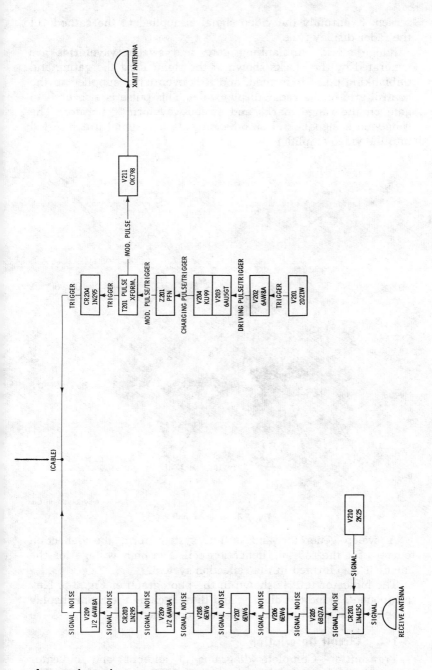

of a complete radar set.

105

screen. Eventually the video signal is applied to the cathode of the radar display tube.

Range marks, unblanking gate, and sweep waveforms are generated by the blocks shown at the right. First the gating and unblanking pulse is formed, and it is eventually supplied to the control grid of the radar display tube. This pulse is also used to gate on the range marks and sweep-waveform generator. The range-mark signals and ship-heading flasher signal are inserted into the video amplifier.

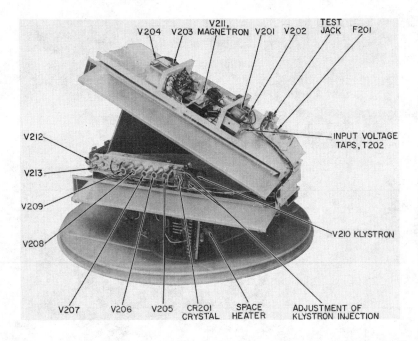

Courtesy Raytheon Co.

Fig. 3-3. Antenna unit.

A sweep generator and output system form the deflection current for the rotating deflection coil. The high voltage for the anode is also formed in the reflection system.

The indicator unit is shown in the photograph of Fig. 3-5. Key components stand out clearly, and these include the radar-display tube and the rotating deflection-coil components.

3-1-2. Circuit Description

Transmitter—Complete diagrams of antenna and indicator systems are given in the schematics of Figs. 3-6 and 3-7. The

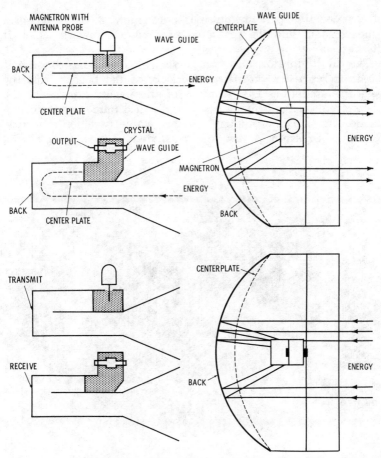

Fig. 3-4. Raytheon dual-antenna system.

master oscillator is a gas-tube type as described in Sec. 2-3-4
The positive trigger pulse removed from the cathode circuit of
the master oscillator is applied to the control grid of the pentode
section of a pentode-triode multivibrator tube (V202). The trigger has a stable 2000-cycle pulse-repetition rate (determined by
the time constant of the gas-tube cathode circuit) that locks the
multivibrator to this frequency. The grid time constant of the
pentode section consists of capacitor C203 and resistor R208. Near
the end of the discharge interval of this combination, the arriving
trigger pulse drives the pentode section into conduction, causing
its plate voltage to drop. At the same time, the screen-grid voltage
drops and the triode section is driven into cutoff, and it remains
at cutoff during the discharge time of capacitor C204. The duration

of the negative pentode pulse is a function of the triode-grid time constant and the regulated plus voltage toward which it discharges.

The multivibrator has two important operating conditions. First, its *repetition rate* is set precisely by the trigger from the gas-tube oscillator. The *duration* of the negative pulse at the plate circuit of the pentode is set by the grid time constant of the triode. This time constant is a highly stable parameter because of the grid-resistor return to a regulated voltage. It is during

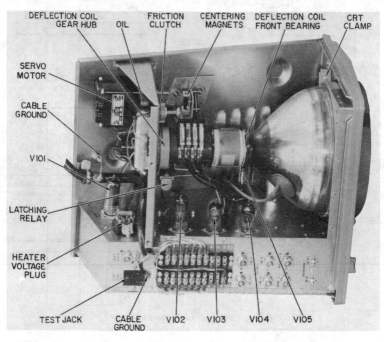

Fig. 3-5. Indicator unit.

this negative pulse interval that the pulse-forming network (Z201) is charged. The extent of the charge is exactly determined by the duration of the multivibrator negative pulse. In fact, the pulse-duration control potentiometer (R213) is called the magnetron-current adjustment because it sets the charge on the pulse-forming network and, indirectly, the magnitude of the modulator pulse.

During the negative pulse, the pentode output tube (V203) is cut off, and the network charges through the charging choke (L202). It charges for the duration of the negative pulse (time

T_1 to T_2). At the conclusion of the negative pulse (time T_2) the pentode conducts and reduces the thyratron plate voltage to a low value. A number of other activities are also initiated at time T_2.

Notice that the negative pulse is also applied through capacitor C261 to a second gas tube (V214). Capacitor C261 and resistor R263 differentiate the pulse waveform, forming a negative leading edge coincident with time T_1 and a positive leading edge coincident with time T_2. It is the positive spike that is of importance.

During the charging time of the network, the gas tube (V214) is cut off and its plate capacitors charge toward the plus B voltage. However, with the arrival of the positive spike V214 is driven into conduction and a high-voltage cathode pulse results. This pulse then triggers the main thyratron tube (V204) which discharges the pulse-forming network across the primary of the pulse transformer (T201). The duration of the pulse across the primary is determined by the delay time of the pulse-forming network. The amplitude of the pulse is dependent on the final charge placed on the network during the charging period.

The trigger thyratron (V214) makes certain that a high-amplitude pulse is applied to the main thyratron. This pulse can reach an amplitude of 300 volts with thyratron conduction, because the cathode circuit attains the voltage of the final charge placed on capacitors C263 and C264. This charge approaches the supply voltage of +350.

After the network has been discharged, the main thyratron must be shut off. This is accomplished by reducing its plate voltage. The plate voltage is dropped when tube V203 is driven into conduction by the positive portion of the applied pulse from the multivibrator which begins its rise, as mentioned previously, at time T_2.

During the discharge of the pulse-forming network across the primary of the pulse transformer, a sharp negative pulse is developed across parallel resistors R255 and R218. This is the trigger pulse supplied to the indicator circuits via the interconnecting cable.

The modulator pulse, which is developed across the dual secondary of the pulse transformer, drives the cathode of the magnetron far negative. The magnetron then oscillates for the duration of the pulse. The resulting microwave pulse is launched toward the transmit-pillbox antenna. The secondary windings of the pulse transformer also function as radio-frequency chokes, and along with capacitors C208 and C209, keep RF out of the filament power source. The voltage drop across resistor R219 can be measured and used as a check of the magnetron current.

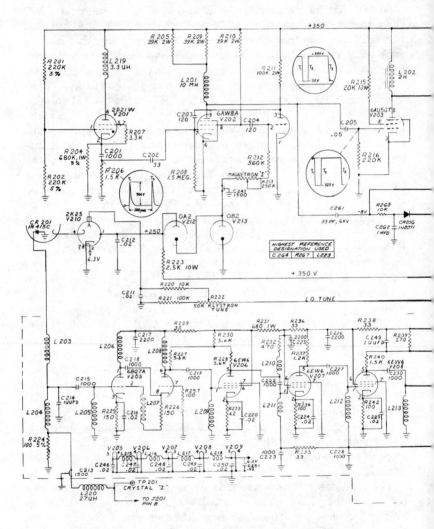

Fig. 3-6. Antenna

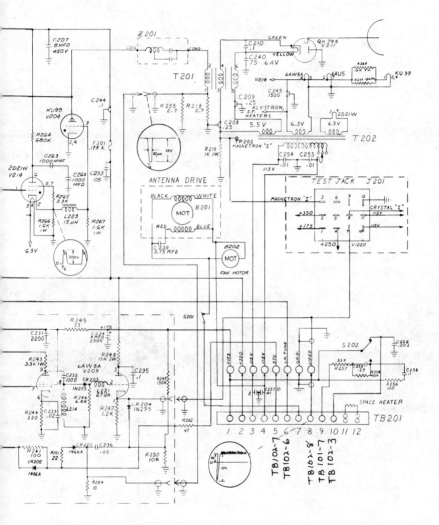

system schematic.

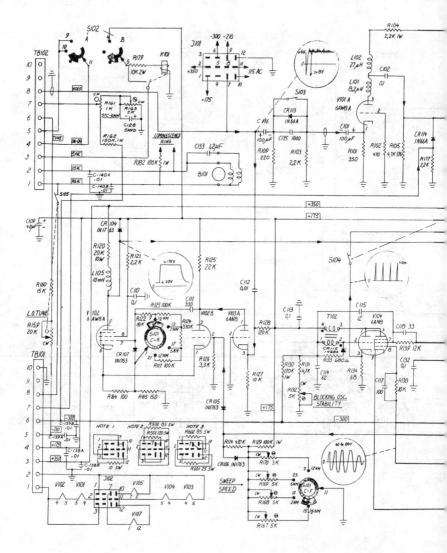

Fig. 3-7. Indicator

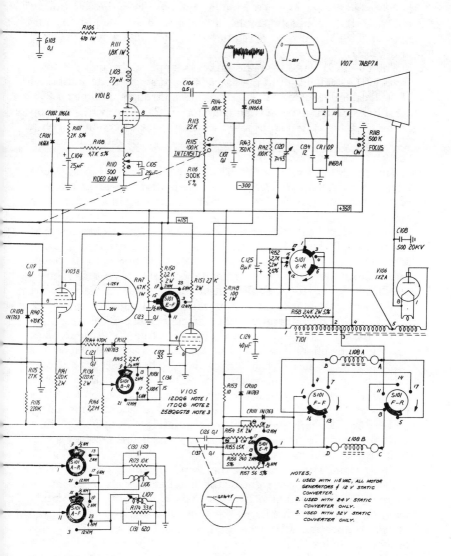

NOTES:
1. USED WITH 115 VAC, ALL MOTOR GENERATORS & 12V STATIC CONVERTER.
2. USED WITH 24V STATIC CONVERTER ONLY.
3. USED WITH 32V STATIC CONVERTER ONLY.

schematic.

Receiver—The receiver is shown at the bottom of the antenna schematic. The klystron local oscillator and the crystal mixer are shown at the left center. The klystron local-oscillator frequency is adjusted by varying its repeller voltage with the LO-tuning controls. It is a highly stable klystron, and its stability is improved with the use of a regulated anode voltage (tubes V212 and V213).

The 30-mc IF output of the mixer is applied through inductor L203 to the grid circuit of the cascode input stage. Four additional IF stages follow. Crystal current flows through inductor L203, RF-filter inductor L204, and resistor R224. The voltage drop across resistor R224 can be used as a measure of crystal current. This crystal-current measurement point is of advantage in tuning the klystron local oscillator.

The crystal detector is CR203. It develops positive-going echo signals across resistor R246; these signals also appear at the grid of the output cathode follower. The positive-going echoes are removed from the cathode and applied through the coaxial video cable to the indicator. Negative-going trigger pulses are inserted via diode CR204. Normally the diode is biased off and does not affect circuit operation. However, when a trigger pulse is developed across the pulse-transformer takeoff, it is strong enough in amplitude to cut through the cut-off bias, and it appears on the cable as a negative trigger of approximately 8 volts.

STC and SHF Operation—The trigger pulse is also applied through diode CR202 to the grid circuit of tubes V207 and V208, biasing them off during transmit time. Furthermore, capacitors C223 and C228 are charged negatively. They discharge slowly through the STC potentiometer (R161) in the indicator circuit. This is the sensitivity time-control circuit which holds down the gain of the IF amplifier during the transmit time and immediately thereafter. The potentiometer, by regulating the discharge time constant, sets the time interval during which the receiver sensitivity is less than maximum.

The circuit associated with the ship's heading flasher (SHF) is located at the lower right of the antenna schematic. A microswitch (S202) is actuated by a cam associated with the rotating antenna. The cam breaks connection with the top contact and makes connection with the bottom fixed contact. When this occurs, capacitor C259 charges through resistor R257 and resistor R177 (between the video amplifier stages of the indicator schematic). During the charge a burst of current flows through resistor R177, developing a positive pulse that is inserted into the video signal via the diode CR114. Normally this diode is biased off by the SHF network. Only during the fast charge of capacitor

C259 does the positive pulse swing far enough to cause diode conduction.

The time constant of the network, including resistor R258, determines the duration of this heading-flasher signal that reaches the cathode of the radar display tube as a negative pulse.

Antenna-Indicator Interconnections—Contacts 5, 6, 8, 9, and 10 of terminal board TB201 have been labeled. Through the cable these terminals connect to the indicated terminals of terminal board 102 or 101 of the indicator schematic (Fig. 3-7). Notice that terminal 9 of TB201 connects to terminal 7 of indicator TB101 from whence it connects to the junction of resistor R177 and diode CR114. Terminal 10 at the antenna terminal board connects to terminal 3 at the indicator board which, in turn, connects to the latching-relay (K101) circuit.

The video signal leaves via terminal 8, connecting to terminal 8 at the indicator. From here the video passes to the input of the video amplifier.

Terminal 5 of the antenna terminal board connects to terminal 7 at the indicator. This terminal connects to the arm of the STC-Gain potentiometer. Its setting determines the shape of the bias-discharge curve for the STC control system. A preset amplifier-gain adjustment is made possible with potentiometer R163, which controls the DC component of the bias that is applied to the bias line.

Terminal 6 of the antenna terminal board connects to terminal 6 at the indicator. This link connects to the local-oscillator tune potentiometer which provides a vernier adjustment of the klystron-repeller voltage.

Indicator—A dual signal is applied to the input of the indicator from the antenna unit. It is a combination video signal and trigger pulse. The source of the video signal is the output cathode follower of the antenna unit, while the trigger pulse is applied to the same output via injection diode CR204. At the input of the video amplifier (left side of capacitor C116) the video signal is positive-going, while the trigger pulse is negative-going.

The video signal of approximately 0.5 volt is increased to 20 volts by the two-stage video amplifier. The input stage is a grounded-grid amplifier, with the input impedance of the tube and resistors R101 and R109 providing a proper impedance match to the 75-ohm coaxial line that transfers the video signal between the antenna unit and the indicator.

When switch S103 is closed, the video signal is applied directly to the cathode of the input-video amplifier. For fast time-constant (FTC) operation, the switch is open. In this case capacitor C135, in conjunction with resistor R103, operates as a differentiating circuit. By so doing, the leading edge of a long-duration target signal is emphasized and is displayed brightly on the screen. The remainder of the target signal is de-emphasized by the differentiating action and is displayed less brightly. Consequently, the target edges are marked off sharply and follow-up information appears with less brightness. There is less spreading of the target blip on the radar screen, and it is possible to obtain sharper demarcation between various incoming target signals. The negative trigger pulse will not be differentiated because it appears negative at the cathode of diode CR113. The pulse causes diode conduction, shunting out the differentiating capacitor C135.

Inasmuch as the first video stage is a grounded-grid amplifier, the target signals appear positive-going in the plate circuit. Good high-frequency response is obtained by the peaking coils and low-value plate resistor R104. A diode is used in the coupling position between the first and second video stages. Normally it is conducting, being forward biased by approximately 1.4 volts. Note that the video signal, which is positive-going, is applied to the cathode of the diode, and it can pass through it. However, any video components in excess of 1.4 volts will then cut off the diode. Thus, the diode operates as a video clipper, cutting off any peaks in excess of approximately 2 volts. This precaution prevents a target from being displayed too brightly on the radar screen. Such excessive brightness can cause "blooming" of a large area of the screen, thus hampering target observations.

The video signal (negative-going) is applied through capacitor C106 to the cathode of the radar tube. Diode CR103 operates as a DC restorer, holding the base line of the video signal at a constant level (+40 volt level) regardless of the noise and target-signal variations. The brightness of the radar display is controlled with the intensity potentiometer (R115), which sets the DC bias applied to the cathode of the radar tube.

Both the range-mark signals and the heading-flasher signal are present in the video signal. As mentioned previously, the heading-flasher signal arrives via diode CR114. Range-mark signals are inserted into the video signal via diode CR101. Both of these signal components are positive-going at the point of insertion. By swinging negative at the cathode of the radar tube, these signals cause an increase in screen illumination.

Gate Multivibrator and Sweep System—The negative trigger pulse is applied to the cathode of the normally cut-off (resistors R128 and R127) trigger tube V103A via capacitor C112. This tube operates as a grounded-grid amplifier, and when it conducts, a negative pulse is developed for application to the bistable gate-pulse multivibrator (V102). Normally V102A is conducting and

V102B is at cutoff because of the high current drawn through the common cathode resistors (R164 and R165).

The negative pulse from the trigger amplifier, arriving via capacitor C111, drives the grid of the first section of V102 to cutoff. The plate current and cathode voltage drop, thus turning on the other section of the multivibrator (V102B). The multivibrator feedback path is completed to the first section of V102 via capacitor C111. The feedback action drives the first section into cutoff and the second section into conduction very quickly. This is the second stable state of the multivibrator. The multivibrator holds at this state until a sawtooth wave, developed in the sweep-output system, reaches a high enough negative voltage to cause diode CR105 to conduct. With diode conduction, tube V102B is driven toward cutoff, and feedback activity returns the multivibrator to its first stable state. It remains in this state until the arrival of the next trigger.

The use of a feedback sawtooth as the so-called "stop trigger" makes certain that the duration of the gate pulse generated by the gate multivibrator corresponds to the desired sweep and range timing. In fact, it is the fedback sawtooth wave that determines the duration of the gate pulse and makes it correspond to the desired range time. It is also necessary that the amplitude of the sawtooth, which sets the length of the trace line, be correct for each operating range. Thus the build-up of the sawtooth must be made to correspond to the desired range time. These requirements are taken care of by section S101C-F of the range switch.

A positive gate pulse, as shown, is removed at the plate of the first section of the multivibrator. It is applied through capacitor C119 to the cathode-follower tube (V103B). The cathode output provides a low impedance source for supplying a positive gate pulse to three individual circuits.

The positive gate is coupled through capacitor C121 to the control grid of the deflection output stage. Capacitor C122 and associated grid resistors provide the necessary waveform delay and shaping to obtain a linear sweep for each range. The output tube acts as a switch and applies an essentially squared wave across the deflection coils (L108A and L108B).

The deflection coils also are switched with S101, according to the desired operating range. Inasmuch as the sweep must begin from the center of the PPI display tube, a DC component must be present in the deflection coil. This DC component is rectified by diode CR111, which in connection with resistors R154 through R157 provides center starting for each range.

When the output tube is shut off at the end of the gate pulse, the deflection field collapses and develops one alternation of a very high voltage oscillation. A stepped-up high-amplitude spike appears across transformer T101 and is rectified by diode D106 to provide the high anode voltage for the radar display tube. This flyback supply is similar to those used in television receivers. Range switch sections S101E-F and S101G-R make the necessary changes in the operating constants of the output stage to establish the proper sweep current and anode voltage regardless of the operating range.

The positive gate pulse at the cathode of tube V103B is also applied to the control grid of the radar tube. This pulse serves as a positive unblanking pulse that turns on the electron beam during the active trace interval. A clipping diode maintains the unblanking pulse at the proper amplitude, and adjustable capacitor C120 and the associated circuit is used to shape the unblanking pulse for optimum operation.

Range-Mark Generation—The range marks are generated by tube V104. The pentode section is a keyed Hartley oscillator. The grid-cathode resonant circuit is set according to the desired range of operation. It is the positive gate pulse from the cathode-follower that turns on the oscillator by applying a positive screen-grid voltage. The Hartley circuit will oscillate for the duration of the applied gate pulse. The two plates are common, and therefore the oscillations are coupled into the monostable blocking-tube circuit (triode section of tube V104).

The blocking tube is normally held at cutoff by its grid-bias network. However, the negative alternations of the Hartley oscillations as they appear at the plate of the pentode drive the grid of the blocking tube positive because of the polarity reversal of transformer T102. When the blocking tube conducts, there is a fast feedback tube activity which quickly drives the grid to the limiting level, as per normal blocking-tube operation. During the conducting interval a sharp short-duration pulse is developed across the cathode resistor. This sharp short-duration pulse is the range-mark signal which is coupled into the video amplifier via diode CR101.

Sweep and Antenna Rotation Synchronization—Antenna rotation and deflection-coil rotation are synchronized in an unusual manner. Two synchronous motors rotate at the same speed. These motors are B201 at the antenna (refer to Figs. 3-6, 3-8 and 3-9) and B101 at the indicator (refer to Figs. 3-5, 3-7, and 3-8). Inasmuch as the two motors rotate at the same speed, they need only be phased correctly to establish a synchronized system. The phasing is accomplished by momentarily stopping the deflection-coil rotation and permitting the antenna rotation to catch up to the same phase.

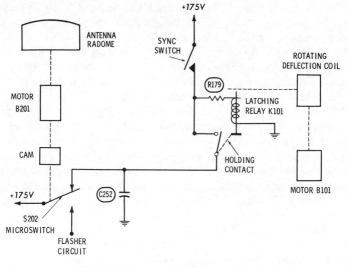

Fig. 3-8. Antenna-sweep synchronization.

In the following explanation locate the various components on the photographs and in the schematics. Note that the latching relay, motor, bearings, clutch, etc., can be seen in Fig. 3-5. The four slip rings for applying sweep current can also be observed.

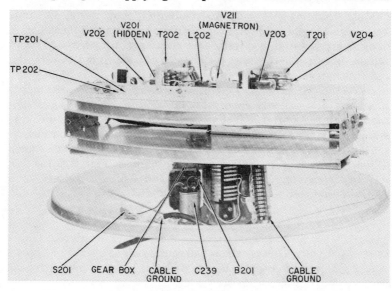

Fig. 3-9. Rear view of antenna unit.

When the antenna sync switch (S102) is held to its sync position, the latching relay (K101) stops deflection-coil rotation. The spring-loaded switch must be released immediately after the relay has locked the deflection coil at a setting with the trace line up (ship's heading). The relay will then hold itself because of the current drawn through its own holding contacts and the normally closed microswitch (S202) at the antenna.

When the antenna passes through zero degree (ship's heading) microswitch S202 opens for a short interval of time. With the contact break the latching-relay circuit is opened and the deflection coil begins to rotate in synchronism with the antenna. Switch S202 closes again after only a few degrees. However, the latching relay will not energize again because the holding contact has been broken. It will not energize again until the spring-loaded sync switch is again set to its synchronizing position. However, microswitch S202 opens each time the antenna passes through zero degrees. As covered previously, whenever this occurs it closes the ship's heading-flasher circuit and the heading flasher is made visible on the radar screen. Therefore, the flash occurs when the sweep line points in the direction of the ship's heading.

Three power supplies are available for the radar set. These are 150 volts AC, 12 volts DC, and 32 volts DC.

3-1-3. Radar Maintenance

Radar sets vary greatly in degree of complexity, sectional arrangement, and individual stage designs. A complete instruction book is an essential accessory to a radar set. Know what is contained in the appropriate book before performing substantial maintenance on any radar set.

Nevertheless, there are certain basic adjustments that apply to almost all radar sets. Key test points and service jacks are common in most radar sets. These provide convenience in checking supply voltages as well as key operating currents and outputs.

In the case of the Model 1900 radar, the test jacks are shown schematically for the indicator and antenna in Figs. 3-6 and 3-7, and in the photographs of Figs. 3-3 and 3-5. The voltages and currents that can be checked are as follows:

1. +175V DC T/R and Ind.
2. +350V DC T/R and Ind.
3. Magnetron Current T/R
4. −250V DC Reg. T/R
5. −210V Reg. Ind.
6. −300V Ind.
7. Tuning (Video) T/R and Ind.

8. Crystal Current T/R
9. Not used
10. 115V AC T/R and Ind.
11. 115V AC T/R and Ind.
12. Ground T/R and Ind.

Many radar sets include their own service meters, as shown in Fig. 3-10. The plug from this meter can be inserted into either the antenna or indicator test jack to make the required measure-

Fig. 3-10. Radar service meter.

ments. If no service meter is available, a conventional multimeter can be employed. Crystal current can be read with a 100-micro-ampere current meter. A rectifier circuit (Fig. 3-11) must be inserted between the video output and the current meter when *tuning* adjustments are made.

Most of the test points check AC and DC supply voltages. The crystal current can be read at terminal 8 of the test jack. As per the antenna schematic, the voltage drop across resistor R224 is a measure of the current drawn by mixer crystal CR201. Its value

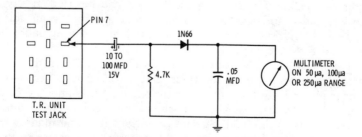

Fig. 3-11. Rectifier-filter for DC output-level measurement.

is a function of the local-oscillator component coupled into the mixer cavity from the klystron cavity. The crystal current can also be measured at test point TP201 located at the rear of the antenna unit (Fig. 3-9).

The magnetron current is related to the voltage drop across resistor R219 in the secondary circuit of pulse transformer T201. It can be measured at terminal 3 of the test jack or at test point TP202 (Fig. 3-9).

The video output of the receiver is connected to terminal 7 of the test jack. The test meter includes a crystal rectifier and filter that develops a DC output corresponding to the signal level at this point. In lieu of the test meter, a crystal rectifier and filter such as that shown in Fig. 3-11 is used. A video output test position is also included in the indicator video amplifier, supplying a test signal to terminal 7 of the indicator test jack.

Convenient test points are of particular help in locating faults. They permit a rapid check of important supply voltages, a process that can quickly isolate a trouble to a power source or to a section of the radar set that is placing an abnormal load on one of the supply-voltage lines.

The magnetron current reading will be abnormal with most magnetron oscillator or modulator faults. Crystal current is a direct indicator of the performance of the klystron local oscillator and crystal mixer injection. Crystals must be replaced because of a deterioration in performance, which is usually made evident by a rise in noise level or an abnormal crystal current.

The two output-measurement points tell about the operation of the receiver and the indicator. They can be used to isolate a signal deficiency to the antenna unit or to the indicator unit.

An oscilloscope is a useful radar test instrument. It can be used to isolate the more obscure troubles when a radar set is being bench-serviced. Receiver output can be monitored conveniently at terminal 7 of the antenna-unit test jack. The make-up of the signal in the indicator can be monitored at terminal 7 of the indicator test jack. Of course the oscilloscope can be used in any of the key pulse and waveform circuits, and a comparison can be made with the key waveforms presented on the schematic diagrams of Figs. 3-6 and 3-7.

Mechanical Considerations—In any radar installation there are certain mechanical considerations that must be met because of movement and the hazards of corrosion. All units and the interconnecting cables must be electrically connected to the common ground point of the boat. Special provisions must be made when units are mounted on wooden bulkheads, and wherever grounding is questionable. Usually the mounting hardware cannot be relied on as a sufficient ground because of the presence of corrosion and dirt, and the possibility of loosening. In addition to the regular mounting hardware, bonding straps are advisable. These straps should be kept as short as possible.

The unit should be kept clean; cleaning should be done with a vacuum cleaner or a clean, dry cloth. High-voltage points are particularly subject to the collection of dust and oil. Tube pins and fuse ends should be checked on a regular basis for clean, good contacts. Relay contacts, slip rings, and brush blocks must be inspected and cleaned periodically. A good grade of oil must be used to lubricate certain mechanical parts. Always refer to the appropriate instruction book for lubrication guidance.

Transmitter-Receiver Adjustments—The adjustment procedures vary substantially among radar designs. One must again refer to the instruction manual for the individual set. However, there are certain basic adjustments that are appropriate to all radar sets.

The magnetron circuit must be adjusted for optimum operation. If a fixed-tuned magnetron is being used, the principal adjustment involves the magnitude of the modulator pulse. In the case of the Model 1900 radar, this adjustment is made with the magnetron current potentiometer (R213) in the grid circuit of the transmit-pulse multivibrator. The current is monitored at terminal 3 of the test jack and is set to some precise value.

If the magnetron is a tunable type, it can be set on frequency with a micrometer-type frequency meter. Echo boxes can also be used as a measure of relative power output and make-up of the transmit pulse.

A second universal objective in the adjustment of a radar set is to have the local oscillator and mixer operate in optimum fashion. By so doing the best signal-to-noise ratio and highest stability can be obtained. The adjustments involve proper crystal current and proper output. Usually the adjustments are made to obtain maximum crystal current and maximum signal output simultaneously.

The local oscillator must be made to operate efficiently, as indicated by a proper peak crystal current. At the same time its oscillating frequency must be such that the IF signal going into the IF amplifier is matched to the IF frequency of the amplifier. This is the basic reason that both crystal-current and receiver-output test points are needed. Adjustments are made for peak current readings at both points.

A special tuning tool is generally provided for resonating the cavity of the klystron local oscillator (Figs. 3-3 and 3-9). The repeller voltage is adjusted with potentiometer R222 of the antenna schematic. Klystron-cavity and crystal-current adjustments are jockeyed for peak crystal current and receiver output.

Indicator Tuning—A number of indicator adjustments are of concern. The sweep must be set up on each range. Usually there are individual preset sweep adjustments for each range. Some of these adjustment points can be seen in Fig. 3-5. There must not be any sweep overshoot at the center (each individual trace should sweep out from the exact center of the radar display tube). The last range-mark ring can be used in setting the individual sweep speeds. In the case of the Model 1900, the sweep speed controls are adjusted until the last range ring appears approximately ¼ inch inside the bearing scale. Actual adjustment procedures vary substantially among radar sets of differing design.

The range-ring generating circuits must be tuned and stabilized. They can then be used as an aid in adjusting the video amplifier and CRT circuits for good clarity and brightness.

Finally, the specialized circuits, such as SHF and STC, are set up for optimum operation. The receiver IF gain control and STC controls are usually adjusted simultaneously to attain maximum sensitivity for operation beyond a desired range limit and less-than-normal sensitivity for close-in targets.

Synchronism of Antenna and Sweep Trace Rotation—The procedure for locking in the antenna and trace line rotations also varies greatly. The steps depend on the type of indicator sweep used and the associated method of synchronous operation. Again it is a matter that is best learned by referring to the instruction book of the specific radar set. The procedure for the Model 1900 was covered in section 3-1-2 under the topics "STC and SHF Operation" and "Sweep Antenna Rotation Synchronization."

3-2. RCA COMPACT MARINE RADAR

The RCA 3.2-cm, 2-kw marine radar to be described is a three-unit arrangement, as shown in the installation diagram of Fig. 3-12. A photograph of the indicator was given previously in Fig. 1-16. The indicator is small and compact, and uses a printed-wiring board type of construction.

The antenna unit mounts only the antenna proper and the rotational components. The remainder of the equipment is contained in a single case that can be mounted at an out-of-the-way location. Specifications for the unit are given in Table 3-2.

As shown in Fig. 3-12, the indicator is connected to the transmitter/receiver via a single multiconductor cable. A second multiconductor cable connects the transmitter/receiver to the rota-

Table 3-2. Electrical Specifications

Range Scales . . . . ½, 1½, 6, 18 miles (nautical or statute)
Range Resolution . . . . 20 yards
Bearing Presentation . . . . Relative with fixed scale
Bearing Resolution . . . . 3.2 degrees
Heading Indication . . . . Scribed illuminated line from center to 0 degree mark
Scope Size . . . . 7" Cathode ray tube
Pulse Length . . . . 0.1 and 0.25 microsecond
Repetition Rate . . . . Varies from 2000 cycles on ½ mi. range
to 1100 cycles on 18 mi. range
Frequency . . . . 9400 mc (3.2 cm) band
Peak Power Output . . . . 3 kw
Ship's Power Supply . . . . 12, 24, 32 volts DC, 110 volts DC
or 115 volts, 50/60 cycle, single phase
Power Drain . . . . Approximately 370 watts for DC and AC, 120 watts on standby
Beam Width . . . . 3.2 degrees horizontal, 20 degrees vertical
Antenna Rotation Speed . . . . 25 rpm
Electronic Range Rings . . . . 1 on ½ mile; 3 on 1½ mile; 6 on 6 and 18 mile

tional components of the antenna. The ½" by 1" wave guide connects transmitter/receiver to antenna.

3-2-1. Functional Block Diagram

The functional block diagram is given in Fig. 3-13. The multivibrator at left center is the master oscillator of the radar set. The multivibrator supplies signal to a multistage sweep-generating circuit, and it also drives the delay-gate generator. The delay-gate operation provides some slight delay between the start of the sweep and the start of other circuit activities. In so doing it is possible to obtain a more linear, center-starting trace line for the radar display tube.

The gate pulse is present at the output of the squaring amplifier, and it supplies signal, as is customary, to various key circuits of the radar set. In the trigger generator a trigger pulse for the transmitter modulator is formed. Simultaneously, via a clamper, an unblanking pulse is applied to the control grid of the display tube.

The output of the squaring amplifier also supplies signals for two other circuits. One component goes to the range-ring oscillator, followed by the range-ring amplifier. The output of the amplifier is supplied to the input of the video amplifier. The squaring amplifier also supplies a gate to the STC generator which is a wave-shaping circuit that develops the STC component for the bias line of the receiver IF amplifier.

The trigger pulse from the trigger generator locks in the modulator blocking oscillator. The blocking oscillator drives the follow-up modulator which develops a high-amplitude negative

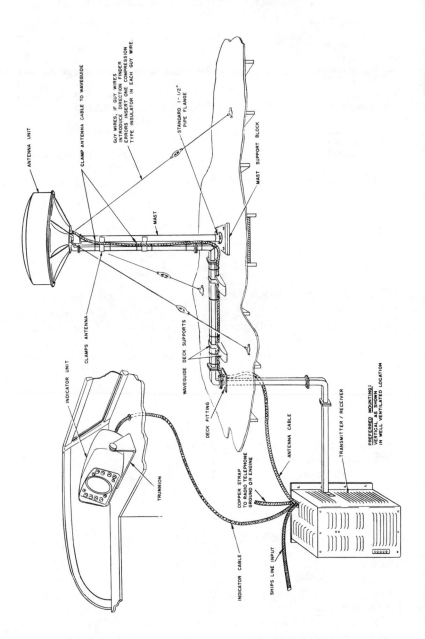

Fig. 3-12. Installation plan of small marine radar.

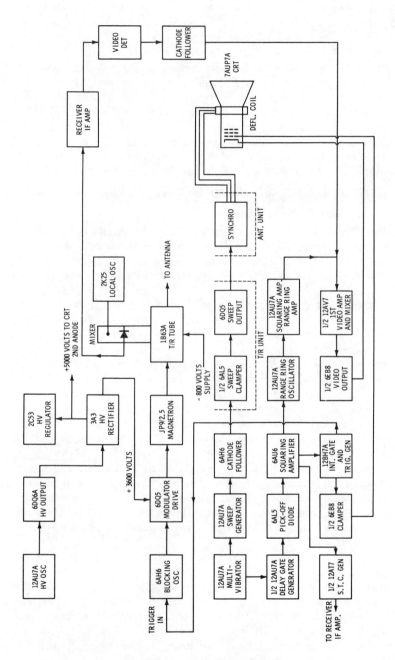

Fig. 3-13. Functional block diagram.

127

pulse that is applied directly to the magnetron oscillator. The four blocks at the top left generate the high voltages for both the modulator and the CRT circuits.

The magnetron output is supplied to the antenna through a duplexer. Returning echoes are picked up by the same antenna and are applied through the duplexer to the crystal mixer. Local-oscillator injection is made into the crystal chamber, and a conversion is made to the IF frequency. A nine-stage amplifier follows. The echoes are demodulated by a crystal video detector, and a succeeding cathode follower transforms the signal to a low impedance for transfer to the video-amplifier input of the indicator. The video-output stage supplies echo and range-mark signals to the cathode of the radar display tube.

3-2-2. Circuit Description

In this section various specialized circuits of the radar set are discussed. These circuits differ from those described previously. Many of the more conventional stages of the radar set were described in the various basic radar circuits which are covered in Chapter 2.

Modulator and High-Voltage Circuits—The modulator and high-voltage circuits are shown schematically in Fig. 3-14. The basic pulse generator is a blocking-tube oscillator which is synchronized by a trigger pulse from the indicator circuits. A positive pulse is removed from the third winding of the blocking-tube transformer and is applied to the control grid of the power-output tube. The output tube is a high-voltage high-current tube similar to those used in the horizontal-output stage of a television receiver. A high-voltage negative pulse is developed in the plate circuit and is capacitively coupled to the cathode circuit of the magnetron.

In this modulator system there is no artificial delay line used to form the modulator pulse. The magnitude of the modulator pulse is preset to the optimum value by the grid-bias potentiometer (1R40). The duration of the pulse is determined by the characteristics of the blocking-tube oscillator and its RC grid-circuit time constant.

For the ½- and 1½-mile range positions, the duration of the transmit pulse is 0.1 microsecond. However, a longer-duration pulse is advantageous for obtaining stronger return signals from the 6- and 18-mile ranges. In this case the pulse duration is increased to 0.25 microsecond. This is accomplished by relay 1K1, which inserts an additional parallel capacitor (1C27) into the grid-circuit time constant. In so doing the pulse-repetition rate is reduced and the pulse duration is increased.

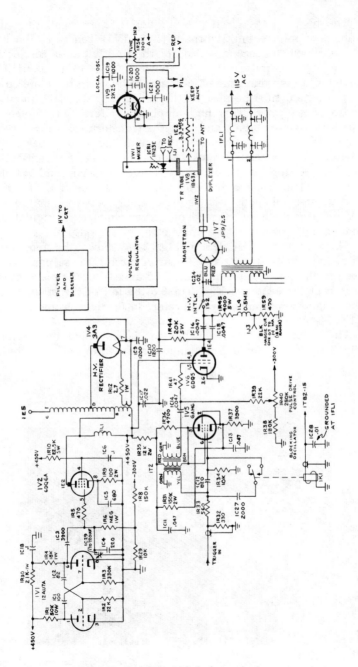

Fig. 3-14. Modulator and duplexer circuits.

The high-voltage circuit is unique; it is an oscillating high-voltage supply. A multivibrator (tube 1V1) generates the basic pulse. When the second section of the multivibrator conducts, a sharp negative pulse drives the power-output tube to cutoff. In so doing, a high-amplitude oscillation develops in the plate circuit of the output tube because of the collapse of the field about the pulse transformer. This high-amplitude alternation, which appears between points A and B of the transformer, is increased in amplitude by the autotransformer action, and it appears as a high-amplitude positive pulse at the anode of the high-voltage rectifier. A filter circuit and high-voltage bleeder assembly follow. Five thousand volts is made available for the radar CRT circuit, and a lesser voltage is used as plate-supply potential for the modulator power-output stage. This latter voltage is regulated to maintain a constant level of magnetron power output.

Magnetron and Duplexer—Fig. 3-14 shows the magnetron, duplexer arrangement, and klystron circuit; these can also be seen in the photographs of Figs. 3-15 and 3-16. The magnetron is shown at the center of Fig. 3-15. To the left of the magnetron is the magnetron filament transformer; to its right is the line filter (1FL1).

The output side of the magnetron is shown at the center of Fig. 3-16. The wave guide is flange-connected to the cavity output

Fig. 3-15. Magnetron and modulator components.

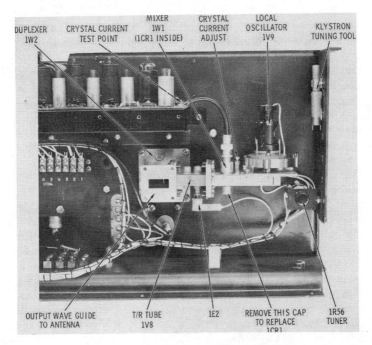

DUPLEXER 1W2 — CRYSTAL CURRENT TEST POINT — MIXER 1W1 (1CR1 INSIDE) — CRYSTAL CURRENT ADJUST — LOCAL OSCILLATOR 1V9 — KLYSTRON TUNING TOOL

OUTPUT WAVE GUIDE TO ANTENNA — T/R TUBE 1V8 — 1E2 — REMOVE THIS CAP TO REPLACE 1CR1 — 1R56 TUNER

Courtesy Radio Corporation of America

Fig. 3-16. Duplexer and local-oscillator components.

of the magnetron. In this photograph you can also see the duplexer, the crystal mixer mount, and the klystron local oscillator. A portion of the receiver IF amplifier is shown at the top left. The klystron repeller-voltage *tune* control is shown at the bottom right. These various components are also shown in the schematic diagram in Fig. 3-14.

The magnetron output is supplied through the duplexer to the wave guide feeding the antenna. For transmit operation the TR tube blocks the input to the receiver. The keep-alive voltage is supplied through resistor 1E2. This connection of the keep-alive voltage can be seen in the photograph immediately to the right and below the wave guide output of the magnetron. The mixer-crystal mount is immediately to the right of the flange joint. A short length of coaxial cable connects the crystal mixer output to the input of the IF amplifier. The crystal current adjustment is to the right of the crystal mount. This adjustment sets the local-oscillator injection. The klystron is on the right side of the duplexer assembly.

Antenna and Indicator Sweep Synchronism—The antenna and rotation components are shown in Fig. 3-17. A schematic diagram of the arrangement is given in Fig. 3-18. The drive motor and gears can be seen below the antenna proper. The synchro generator is on the right side of the assembly.

The synchro generator is tied to the radar-tube sweep system in the manner shown in Fig. 3-18. In the more elaborate servo system described in Chapter 2, the output of the synchro generator is applied to a synchro transformer, a servo amplifier, and finally to the synchro motor. In this small compact marine radar unit the three stator windings of the synchro generator are connected to similar star-connected deflection-coil windings.

The actual deflection current is supplied to the rotor of the synchro generator (mounted at the antenna). This rotor is also rotated by the antenna drive motor through a gearing arrangement. As a result, the voltages induced into the stator windings are a function of the sweep current and the antenna rotation. These variations are transferred to the deflection coil windings. Here their changing fields influence the scanning beam as it travels between the electron-gun output and the fluorescent screen of the radar tube. The arrangement is not unlike that of a synchro repeater with the exception that the changing fields from the stator windings, instead of inducing a current into a winding, control the deflection of a beam of electrons. In this case the sweep-deflection currents initially applied to the rotor at the synchro generator cause the beam to move from the center position to the outer periphery. The fact that the synchro-generator rotor also turns with the antenna causes the scanning beam to

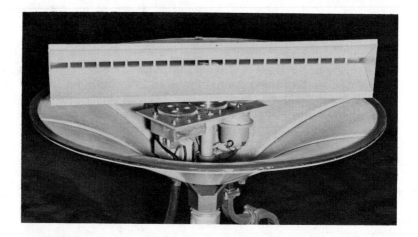

Courtesy Radio Corporation of America

Fig. 3-17. Radar-antenna assembly.

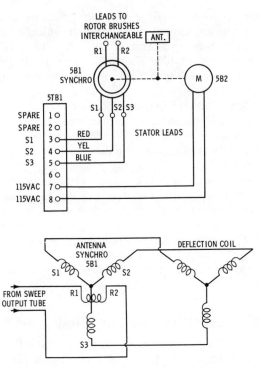

Fig. 3-18. Antenna and sweep synchronization.

rotate in a similar manner, and as a result, the trace line revolves around the fluorescent screen.

3-2-3. Maintenance

The same general objectives and key adjustments apply as covered in Sec. 3-1. Specific procedures are always given in the appropriate instruction book for the particular radar set.

Antenna and Sweep Trace Orientation—Proper phasing between sweep trace and antenna rotation can be accomplished either by rotating the deflection coil or by adjusting the antenna reflector. With the radar system in operation a target should be located at a known angle to the ship's heading, preferably dead ahead. The deflection coil clamp is loosened and the coil is rotated until the target appears at the proper angle.

Alternately, the indicator sweep can be stopped when it is pointing in the direction of a known target. The radar cover can now be removed and the set screws of the reflector loosened. The reflector is now moved until the target is displayed on the stopped trace of the indicator screen.

Modulator-Magnetron—First the high voltages are set, using the adjustments associated with the high-voltage multivibrator and the high-voltage regulator circuit. A 0-10 milliammeter is connected at test point 1J3. The pulse-drive control potentiometer (1R40) is then adjusted for a maximum magnetron-current reading.

Crystal Mixer and Klystron Oscillator—Adjust the mixer-oscillator circuit by connecting the current meter to the crystal-current test point shown in Fig. 3-16. Adjustments are made with the indicator tune control set to midpoint.

For the initial tuneup the klystron tool (Fig. 3-16) is used to close the cavity strut of the klystron. Gradually open the strut and rotate the repeller tune control (1R56) back and forth until crystal current shows on the meter. Sometimes it is necessary to adjust the tuning screw in the wave guide to obtain a current reading. With a crystal-current reading present, open the strut slowly until the target appears. Continue to adjust the strut until a maximum target occurs coincident with maximum crystal current.

3-3. TRANSISTOR NAVIGATIONAL RADAR SET

The transistor is proving its worth by reducing the weight and size of radio navigational equipment, including radar. A prototype of a transistor radar unit has been designed by the Fairchild Semiconductor Corporation (Fig. 3-19). In addition to the radar scope tube, the only tubes in the set are associated with the RF section—namely, magnetron, TR and ATR, and klystron local oscillator. The pulse power is 10-kw peak, even though the total weight of the equipment is only 40 pounds; this unit compares to all-tube versions of comparable power with weights in excess of 100 pounds.

As shown in Fig. 3-20, it is a two-unit affair with the antenna system being an inherent part of the transmitting unit. However, suitable wave-guide hardware would permit the separate mounting of the antenna system.

A 93-kc oscillator is the master timer, or clock, of the system. Through a suitable counting chain a pulse rate of 930 PRF is attained. A 930-cycle trigger pulse is used to drive the pulse modulator in the transmitting unit. The output of the pulse modulator fires the magnetron. The microwave pulse of energy is coupled to the antenna through the duplexer. Returning target signals are heterodyned down to a 60-mc IF frequency with a crystal diode mixer and klystron local oscillator. Three transistor IF stages follow.

Fig. 3-19. Transistor navigation radar.

The IF signal is further amplified at the indicator by three IF stages. These stages are followed by a crystal detector and a two-stage video amplifier.

The video signal, unblanking or "intensifying" pulse, and range marks are applied to the CRT grid-cathode circuit. The indicator circuitry develops the range-mark signal, sweep waveform, and unblanking pulse.

The radar set has been designed for 5- and 25-mile range operation. Internal photographs of transmitting and indicator units are given in Figs. 3-21 and 3-22.

3-3-1. Circuit Descriptions

Pulse Modulator and Magnetron Circuits—The modulator consists of three 400-volt silicon-controlled rectifiers in a series arrangement (Fig. 3-23). Since a resonant charging arrangement is used (charging choke L_c and pulse-forming line), more than 900 volts appears across the SCR pulse-modulator circuit.

The trigger pulse is able to fire the sensitive SCR semiconductor devices directly. The low-powered trigger pulse at the SCR gates is able to switch a 66-ampere collector-current flow.

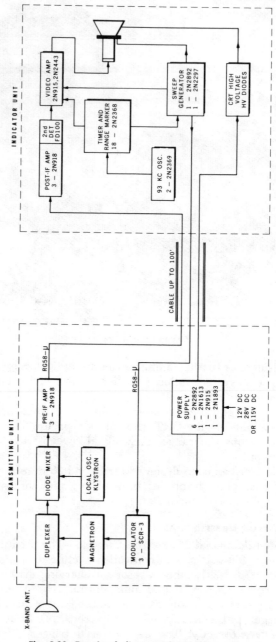

Fig. 3-20. Functional diagram of transistor radar.

Fig. 3-21. Transmitting unit.

Fig. 3-22. Indicating unit.

It is apparent that the weight and size of the pulse modulator can be greatly reduced with the use of SCR's as compared to the conventional thyratron switches and vacuum-tube power amplifiers.

If we assume the magnetron is operating with a 40-percent efficiency, it is necessary to develop a 5.5-kilovolt pulse at a peak current of 4.5 amperes to obtain a pulse power output of 10 kw.

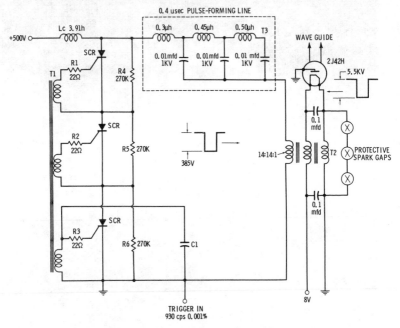

Fig. 3-23. SCR modulator and magnetron.

The modulator must then be expected to supply a peak pulse power of 25 kw. The turns ratio of the pulse transformer is such that the low impedance of the 6.81-ohm primary (450V/66A) is matched to the magnetron loading of 1220 ohms (5500V/4.5A). The duration of the pulse is 0.4 microsecond as determined by the pulse-forming line. Wth a PRF rate of 930 per second, the duty cycle becomes 372×10^{-6}. Average output power is then 3.72 watts.

Various key components can be seen on the transmitter photograph (Fig. 3-21), including the power transformer and other power components, duplexer and the magnetron at the lower right. The three-stage IF amplifier is shown at the lower left.

IF Amplifier and Detector—The crystal mixer, a representative transistor IF amplifier, and the crystal AM detector are shown

138

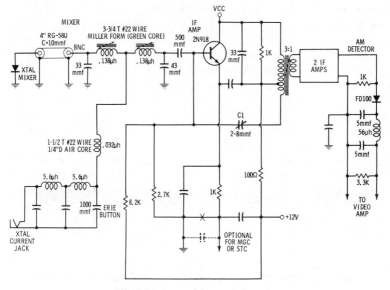

Fig. 3-24. IF amplifier and detector.

in Fig. 3-24. A double-tuned transformer is used to match the output of the crystal to the low-impedance input of the first IF stage. The path for the DC crystal current is through the crystal metering circuit and the appropriate IF filter.

The IF amplifier consists of two sets of stagger-tuned triple amplifiers (triples). One set is shown in Fig. 3-24. The stages are transformer-coupled. The primary winding is tapped to provide a feedback voltage that can be used for neutralization. A capacitor (C1) is used in each stage to neutralize the stages individually. Each stage has a bandwidth of 11.6 mc to obtain an overall 10-mc bandwidth. The total gain of the two triples is more than 120 db. A 2-microvolt input signal would produce more than a 2-volt IF signal for application to the crystal AM detector. Positive-going video signals are made available across the diode load resistor.

In the IF amplifier the STC voltage is applied to the base circuit of the second amplifier. A manual gain-control voltage (MGC) is applied to the base circuit of the third IF stage. The method of base feed of STC or MGC bias is shown in the optional connection in Fig. 3-24.

Video Amplifier—A simple two-stage video amplifier builds up the output of the video detector to the 40 volts needed to drive the cathode of the 7-inch CRT tube. Thus an input signal of 2 volts as derived at the output of the video detector will be amplified to a voltage level in excess of 40, thus providing adequate drive for the radar display tube. The input stage (Fig. 3-25) is a common-collector type used mainly for impedance matching and isolation. Voltage gain is set by a common-emitter output stage.

The common-collector input stage presents a high impedance to the output of the video detector and, therefore, minimum loading. At the same time, its output impedance is low and there is a preferred constant voltage drive of the common-emitter output stage. Thus the Miller effect of the voltage amplifier is not reflected to the output of the video detector where it could influence the overall bandwidth of the system.

The output stage is biased to near cutoff by resistor R7 and forward-biased diode D3 and its associated time constant capacitor C4. Biasing the output stage to near cutoff (minimum collector-current flow) means that the collector voltage can be made to swing between the collector supply voltage and the low saturated level of collector voltage. It might be expected that the transfer characteristic of the stage would be nonlinear at low base-input voltage. However, the signal present in the input of the common-emitter stage consists of the signal plus the intensifying gate signal (unblanking pulse). It is this pulse that causes the collector current of the common-emitter transistor to pass very quickly through the low-current, nonlinear region. The video signal is mounted on top of the pedestal supplied by the gate signal, as shown in Fig. 3-25. The amplitude level that the video and range-mark signal occupy corresponds to the linear portion of the common-emitter transfer.

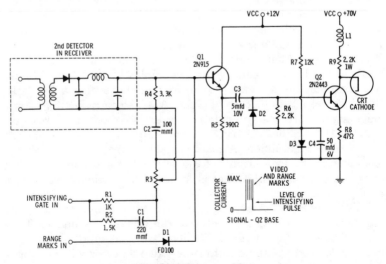

Fig. 3-25. Video amplifier.

The amplitude of the intensifying gate pulse at the cathode of the CRT tube reaches a level at which the electron beam will just be turned on. The video signal swings to an even higher negative voltage at the cathode, and therefore the beam intensity is always increased with the presence of video or range-mark signals.

In addition to the video signal from the output of the video detector, both the intensifying gate and the range-mark signals are applied to the base circuit of the common-collector input stage. The level of the gate pulse can be set with potentiometer R3. The crystal detector diode and the range-mark diode operate as an OR circuit. Either one or the other of the two diodes is conducting, depending on which signal has the higher amplitude. Thus during the range-mark signal, diode D1 conducts and the crystal detector diode is cut off. Between range-mark pulses the output of the crystal detector is stronger, and therefore diode D1 is cut off during the video signal time. This OR gate action provides excellent isolation between video-signal source and range-mark signal source.

Diode D2, capacitor C3, and resistor R6 provide clamping action. Their purpose is to polarize the composite signal being applied to the base of the transistor. Polarization is such that the signal swings in a direction that will increase collector current from the near cutoff value set by the diode D3 and resistor R7 combination. D2 conducts between intensifying gate pulses and keeps the base of Q2 at the negative potential set by the charge placed on capacitor C4. When an intensifying gate signal arrives, diode D2 goes out of conduction, and the Q2 collector current rises from its near cutoff value.

The output of Q2 is direct coupled to the cathode of the radar tube. No clamping is required because of direct coupling. High frequencies are maintained by the low value of the collector resistor (R9) and the shunt peaking inductor (L1).

Indicator Circuits—The indicator circuits are unusual, and they show a definite departure from the conventional radar method. They represent a trend in radar circuit design. The master oscillator is crystal controlled on a frequency of 93 kc. All the signal components are indirectly derived from this master signal. This technique provides high accuracy and stability and eliminates factory and field setup adjustments. The 93-kc frequency has a period corresponding to a radar statute mile.

$$\text{Period} = \frac{1}{\text{Frequency}} = \frac{10^6}{93,000} = 10.75 \, \mu \, \text{Sec}$$

$$10.75 \, \mu \, \text{Sec} = 1 \, \text{Statute Radar Mile}$$

It is apparent then that 1-mile range marks can be derived directly from the output of the oscillator.

The oscillator output is counted down to the PRF rate by a 100-to-1 divider chain. The chain consists of a 4-to-1 divider and two 5-to-1 dividers. All of the dividers are of a binary type with the necessary feedback to obtain a net 5-to-1 count from a basic 8-to-1 binary chain.

Additional timing signals are derived from the binary chain. For example, at the output of the 5-to-1 divider the pulse-repetition frequency is 18.6 kc. The period of this wave corresponds to a 5-mile radar-wave excursion. Thus it can be used to generate 5-mile range rings as well as to control the duration of the intensifying pulse and the sweep trace for a 5-mile range setting. The output of the second 5-to-1 divider (total count of 25) can also be used in setting the duration of the intensifying pulse and the sweep trace for 25-mile range operation of the radar set. The trigger pulse for the transmitter is derived from the output of the last counter, providing a 930-cycle gate pulse for firing the transmit modulator.

The 93-kc crystal-oscillator schematic is given in Fig. 3-26. Transistor Q1 is used as the basic oscillator, with transistor Q2 acting as the output transistor and feedback inverter. The crystal is located between the collector circuit of the output stage and the base circuit of the input stage. The crystal operates in its series mode, ensuring maximum feedback at its resonant fre-

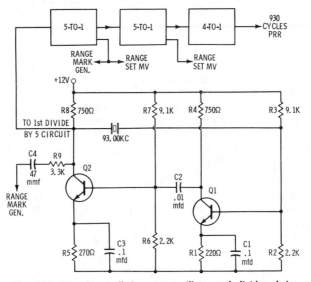

Fig. 3-26. Crystal-controlled master oscillator and divider chain.

quency. This frequency-selective feedback makes certain that the oscillator operates at the crystal frequency.

The output of the oscillator feeds a flip-flop binary counter which develops one output pulse for each two input pulses. Basically this circuit is a bistable multivibrator with the two sides being switched alternately on and off by each two arriving pulses. Similar binary stages follow to obtain a total count of 100 to 1.

Range-Mark Generation—The range-mark circuit is shown in Fig. 3-27. Range marks of 1 mile or 5 miles can be displayed

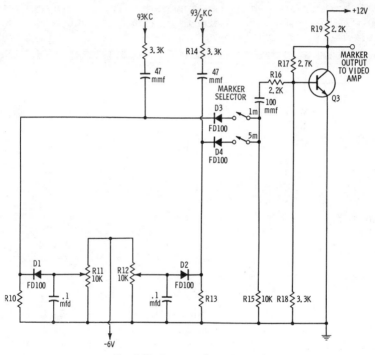

Fig. 3-27. Range-mark generator.

separately or simultaneously. The range-mark circuit receives its signals from the pulse output of the 93-kc oscillator and the output of the first 5-to-1 counter. These pulses are applied to separate differentiating circuits composed of a 47-mmf differentiating capacitor plus associated resistor and diodes. The 1-mile and 5-mile spike amplitudes can be adjusted separately with potentiometers R11 and R12. As established by the diode polarities, the negative spikes are emphasized and applied to the base circuit of the marker amplifier and inverter. Positive marker pips are applied to the input of the first video amplifier (Fig. 3-25).

The 5-mile pips are adjusted to a higher amplitude than the 1-mile pips. Thus when the pips are presented on the radar display tube, the 5-mile rings have a brighter intensity than the 1-mile rings.

The simplicity of the associated circuits should be apparent as compared to the more conventional range-ring circuits and associated shaping stages. Using the divider arrangement there are no range circuit adjustments except for the switching, and the setting of the relative range-marker amplitudes.

Intensity Gate and Sweep Generator—The intensifying gate and sweep system of the transistor radar indicator are shown

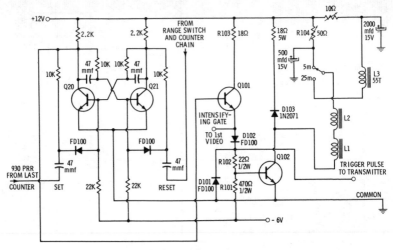

Fig. 3-28. Unblanking pulse and sweep generator.

schematically in Fig. 3-28. The output of the final stage of the final 4-to-1 counter is applied to a transistor flip-flop range-set multivibrator. A negative trigger arrives from the last counter and turns off the first section of the multivibrator, removing it from its one stable state. Feedback drives the second section (Q21) into conduction. During this state, a positive pulse is derived from the collector of the first section. The duration of this pulse corresponds to the radar time associated with either the 5-mile range or the 25-mile range.

Actually the duration of the pulse depends on how soon after its start a second trigger pulse arriving from some other part of the divider chain is applied to the base of the second section of the range-set multivibrator. When the second trigger does arrive, it changes the MV over to the original stable state by driving the second section to cutoff and the first section into conduction.

144

The multivibrator remains in this state until the next trigger arrives from the output of the last counter.

In summary, the range-set multivibrator generates a positive pulse with a frequency of 930 cycles. The duration of the pulse is controlled by a trigger arriving at the second section of the multivibrator from the appropriate time output of the divider chain. In the case of 5-mile range operation this second trigger is derived from the output of the first 5-to-1 counter. For 25-mile operation the duration of the pulse must be longer, and so the second trigger comes from the output of the second 5-to-1 divider.

The positive pulse from the range-set multivibrator is applied to the common-emitter transistor stage (Q101). This stage presents a high impedance to the range-set multivibrator and provides a low-impedance output from which various key pulses are derived. The positive intensifying gate is removed at the emitter of transistor Q101 and is applied to the input of the first video amplifier. A second output is derived at the top of resistor R102 and is supplied as a positive trigger gate pulse to the modulator (Fig. 3-23).

Still another component is applied to the base of the sweep-output transistor (Q102). This transistor operates as a switch. When the positive pulse is applied to its gate, it conducts and develops a strong negative square wave at the collector. As a result of the square wave, there is a linear rise of current in the deflection yoke (L1). Because of the resistance of the yoke and the switch, there is some inherent nonlinearity in the sweep-current sawtooth. However, this nonlinearity is compensated for by a small saturable reactor (L2) in series with the deflection yoke. The saturable reactor compensates for the slowing effect of the resistance on the rise of the sawtooth.

For 25-mile range operation the rise of the sawtooth must be slower, and therefore an additional inductance is switched into the circuit. The amplitudes of the deflection waveforms can be preset with the separate adjustable resistors in the deflection-coil charging circuit.

At the end of the sweep period, the deflection output transistor swings toward cutoff, because of the trailing edge of the gate pulse applied to its base. The energy stored in the collector-circuit inductance must be dissipated between sweeps. This is accomplished with the 18-ohm, 5-watt damping resistor. Diode D103 is polarized so that it conducts only during the current-decay period. During the trace the collector of the deflection output transistor swings negative, and the diode is nonconducting. Thus, the damping resistor is not functioning, and it does not cause a loss in efficiency during the trace interval.

145

CHAPTER 4

Questions and Answers

This chapter covers the Element 8 Ship Radar Technique questions as given in the FCC Study Guide and Reference Material for Commercial Radio Operator Examination. To obtain the radar license endorsement you must pass an examination based on these questions.

Questions and answers have been rearranged for good study continuity. A short, direct answer is given for each question. You are also directed to an appropriate detailed discussion in the handbook. This follow-up study will permit you to acquire a greater depth of understanding, and you will be better prepared for the different ways a question of this type might be presented in a multiple-choice examination. This study process is not only an aid to memory, it also gives you the knowledge you will need when you begin to work on actual radar sets.

It is preferable that you read the initial four chapters of this handbook before beginning work on this Q and A chapter. In particular, spend some extra effort on Chapters 1 and 2, because they treat in detail the topics of a high percentage of the questions that are given in the examination. Additional references are made in the chapter to specific equipment described in Chapter 3 and to the specific radar laws given in the appendix.

4-1. RADAR PRINCIPLES AND LAWS

1. **Draw a block diagram of a radar system, labeling the antenna, duplexer, transmitter, receiver, modulator, timer, and the indicator.**—See Fig. 4-1.
2. **Briefly explain the principle of operation of a radar system.**—The transmitter sends out a pulse of radio-frequency energy to a reflecting target. Some of the reflected energy returns to the radar set and is picked up on the receiver. Since radio waves travel at a constant speed, the radar set, by evaluating the time needed for the radio energy to make a round-trip excursion, determines the distance, or *range*, to the target. The angle at

which the antenna is directed when radar pulses make such a round trip to a target indicates the *bearing* of the target.

The timer (Fig. 4-1) establishes the number of pulses that are sent out each second. In so doing, it also establishes the transmit and receive times of the radar set. Under control of the timing pulse, a power pulse is formed in the modulator. This power-modulator pulse turns the magnetron oscillator on and off at the desired pulse rate. It is the magnetron that forms the burst of microwave RF energy which is fed to the antenna through a duplexer and wave guide. The duplexer provides the necessary isolation to permit one antenna to be used for both transmit and

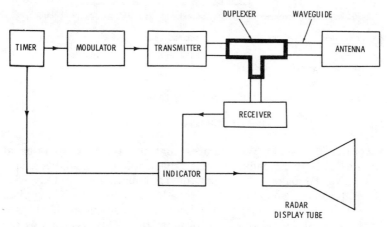

Fig. 4-1. Block diagram of a radar set.

receive. The return signal is fed to the receiver, where it is amplified and detected. It is then passed to the indicator. The indicator, under control of the timing pulses, generates the sweep and calibration waveforms needed by the radar display tube. The return signals are also applied to the radar display tube. The radar tube is a cathode-ray type, and the target information is painted on its fluorescent screen. Range, bearing, and other target attributes can be measured and observed on the display pattern. (Secs. 1-1, 1-2, 1-3, 1-4, and 1-9.)

3. Draw a simple block diagram of a radar duplexer system, labeling the wave guide, TR box, anti-TR box, receiver, and transmitter.—See Fig. 4-2.

4. Briefly describe the construction and operation of radar TR and anti-TR boxes. What is the purpose of a keep-alive voltage?—The TR and anti-TR boxes are inserted in the duplexer to provide optimum isolation between transmitter output

147

and receiver input, making it possible to use a single antenna for transmit and receive. The boxes are usually a part of a wave-guide assembly so that they do not introduce any discontinuity in the signal paths. The TR and ATR tubes themselves are gas diodes which ionize and arc under excitation of the high voltage of the transmit pulse. Thus, both tubes act as short circuits during the transmit pulse.

The TR box shorts the receiver input during the transmit pulse. Therefore, the transmit energy cannot do any damage to the

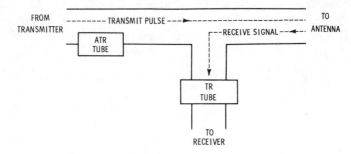

Fig. 4-2. Radar duplexer system.

receiver. The short also ensures that the receiver operates at high sensitivity immediately after the trailing edge of the trans-mit pulse. To make certain that the TR ionizes very quickly with the initiation of the transmit pulse, a keep-alive voltage is applied across the two electrodes. This keep-alive voltage holds the gas in the tube almost at the point of ionization. Thus, as soon as the transmit pulse begins, the TR tube ionizes and blocks the receiver input.

The ATR box is located in the transmit wave-guide path. It also ionizes with the transmit pulse and provides a path of trans-mission from the transmitter to the antenna. During the receive interval, when there is no transmit pulse, the ATR and TR tubes deionize. As a result, a return signal passes without attenuation into the receiver input. Because the ATR tube is deionized, an incoming signal sees a high impedance path toward the trans-mitter. Thus, the incoming signal is shuttled into the receiver instead of the transmit channel. (Secs. 1-9, 1-11-2, 2-2-3, 2-3-5 and 2-4-1.)

5. **What are the FCC license requirements for the operator who is responsible for the installation, servicing, and main-tenance of ship radar equipment?**—The operator or mainte-nance technician that performs or supervises the above proced-ures must hold a first-class or second-class radiotelephone or

radiotelegraph license with a ship radar endorsement. The only replacements that may be made by a person not so licensed are fuses and receiver tubes. RR 83.155.

6. **Who may operate a ship-radar station?**—Operation during the course of normal rendition of service must be performed exclusively by the master of the radar-equipped ship or by one or more of the persons responsible to him and authorized by him to do so. RR 83.155.

7. **Under what conditions may a person who does not hold a radio-operator license operate a ship-radar station?**—Any nonlicensed person may operate the radar provided that the stipulations of RR 83.155 are obeyed. These are: (A) The radar equipment shall employ as its frequency-determining element a nontunable, pulse-type magnetron. (B) The radar equipment shall be capable of being operated with external controls exclusively, in accordance with commission rules and regulations. (C) Operation must be by the master or one or more persons responsible to him and authorized by him to do so. (D) Adjustments and tests must be made by properly licensed personnel. RR 83.155.

8. **Who may make entries in installation and maintenance records of a ship-radar station?**—The responsible operator concerned. RR 83.405.

9. **What entries are required in the installation and maintenance records of a ship-radar station?**—These entries are: (A) Date and place of initial installation. (B) Any necessary steps taken to remedy any interference found to exist at the time of such installation. (C) The nature of any complaint (including interference to radiocommunication) arising subsequent to initial installation and the date thereof. (D) The reason for the trouble leading to the complaint, including the name of any component or component part that failed or was misadjusted. (E) Remedial measures taken, and date thereof. (F) The name, license number, and date of the ship-radar endorsement on the first- or second-class operator license of the responsible operator performing or immediately supervising the installation, servicing, or maintenance. (See Table 4-1.) RR 83.405.

10. **Who has the responsibility for making entries in the installation and maintenance record of a ship-radar station?**—The entries are the responsibility of the operator-licensed installation, service, or maintenance technician concerned in each particular instance, and the station licensee. RR 83.405.

11. **Within what frequency bands do ship-radar transmitters operate?**—2900 to 3100 mc, 5460 to 5650 mc, and 9300 to 9500 mc. RR 83.404.

Table 4-1. Sample radar log

RADAR LOG SS   ESSO PATTERSON

MONTH AND DAY	TIME AM PM	SEA AND WEATHER CONDITIONS, WIND FORCE, VISIBILITY, RAIN, FOG, SNOW CONDITIONS, APPROXIMATE POSITION, COURSE.	UNUSUAL INCIDENTS OF RADAR OPERATION WHERE SAFETY OF VESSEL WAS AIDED OR HINDERED.	ELAPSED TIME HOUR METER READING.
2-10	1244	Wind force 4, moderate sea, visibility 1 mile. Position 120 miles south Ambrose L. V. Course 3 degrees True	Sighted small trawler at 5 miles, bearing 358 degrees True- plotted course 154 degrees, tracked down till bearing 45 degrees True, range 800 yards	325
2-15	0430	Wind force 5, moderate sea, morning haze, visibility $\frac{1}{2}$ mile. Proceeding on course 160° T. Speed 12 approximately 20 miles south Mantanilla Buoy	Contacted target at 7.5 miles two points off port bow at 0525. Visibility now 3 miles. Sighted buoy 2 points forward of port beam at 3 miles (by radar range) 0540. Buoy abeam at 0554, changed course 193° T. Speed 12	417
2-17	1045	Wind force 10, moderate sea, partly cloudy, visibility 7 miles. Position 80 miles southeast of New Orleans course 340° T. Speed 14K	Checked radar operation targets visible on "Scope" out to 24 miles	442
2-18	0930	In port, New Orleans	In port, New Orleans	443

Table 4-1. Sample radar log (Cont'd)

YEAR __1960__

OPERATIONAL FAILURES: DURATION, NATURE AND CAUSE OF EACH FAILURE.	ADJUSTMENTS AND/OR REPAIRS EFFECTED BY SERVICE PERSONNEL.	SIGNATURE, TITLE & PORT. FCC LICENSE NO. DATE OF RADAR ENDORSEMENT.
NONE	NONE	T. Woods, Master
NONE	NONE	J. Walker, 2d Mate
Noted occasional disappearance of fixed range rings. Wired radiomarine office New Orleans requesting service 2-18	NONE	T. Woods, Master
Defective 6SN7 V-1010	Range mark tube low in emission. Replaced tube. Operation of equipment now normal	R. Johnson Radiomarine New Orleans

Courtesy Radio Corporation of America

12. **May fuses and receiving-type tubes be replaced in ship's radar equipment by a person whose operator's license does not contain a ship-radar endorsement?**—Yes. Such a person must be responsible to, or authorized by, the master of the radar-equipped ship. RR 83.155.

4-2. TRANSMITTER AND ANTENNA

1. **Describe how a radar beam is formed by a paraboloidal reflector.**—The antenna or source of microwave energy is mounted at the focus point of a parabolic reflector. (See Figs. 2-12 and 2-13.) The microwave energy is directed onto the reflecting surface. At this point it is reflected forward in parallel rays, forming a small diameter beam. Regardless of the angle of arrival of energy at the reflector from the antenna source, the angle of reflection is such that the rays will be directed in parallel paths. (Sec. 2-1-3.)

2. **Briefly describe the construction of a wave guide. Why should the interior of the wave guide be clean, smooth, and dry?**—Wave guides are constructed of durable weather-resistant metal capable of reflecting microwave energy with a minimum loss. The cross section of the wave guide is rectangular or tubular (Figs. 2-1 and 2-5). There is no inner conductor and the radio-frequency energy propagates along the wave-guide enclosure much as a radio wave is propagated through space. However, it is channeled within the wave guide because of the reflecting inner walls of the guide. These guide walls absorb an insignificant amount of the energy; by suitable dimensioning, they provide an excellent means of guiding a radar pulse from transmitter to antenna, and they also guide a return signal from antenna to receiver input.

The efficiency of the wave guide depends on the uniformity of the inner walls and the completeness with which the waves are reflected from the walls. Therefore the interior should be clean, smooth, and dry. Water, dust, and corrosion will introduce discontinuities that increase the radio-wave attenuation; if the discontinuity is severe, it may damage components or seriously affect the range and performance of the radar set. (Sec. 2-1-1.)

3. **Why are wave guides used in preference to coaxial lines for transmission of microwave energy in most shipboard-radar installations?**—Wave guides have much less loss at microwave frequencies than do coaxial lines. (Sec. 2-1-1.)

4. **Why are rectangular cross-sectional wave guides generally used in preference to circular cross-sectional wave guides?**—The rectangular wave guide can more effectively prop-

agate a single excitation mode, and it is less subject to changes in polarization at junctions and bends. (Secs. 2-1-1 and 2-1-2.)

5. Describe how wave guides are terminated at the radar-antenna reflector.—Usually the end of the wave guide is shaped into a horn or some other type of configuration that will direct the microwave energy onto the reflecting surface and provide the most effective transfer of the signal from the guide to a radiated beam of specific horizontal- and vertical-beam angles. (Secs. 2-1-2 and 2-1-3.)

6. Why are choke joints often used in preference to flange joints to join sections of a wave guide?—With the use of a choke joint an electrical short circuit is reflected to the joint. Although the mechanical joint may not be perfect, the electrical continuity is maintained, and there is minimum signal loss at the junction. (Sec. 2-1-2.)

7. Draw a longitudinal section of a wave-guide choke joint and briefly explain its principle of operation.—Such a choke joint is shown in Fig. 4-3. A quarter-wavelength slot is cut into one of the flanges. This slot is spaced a quarter wavelength from the gap, or joint, between the actual inner walls of the two wave-guide sections. It acts as a half-wavelength section of line short-circuited at the closed end of the slot. At the frequency of operation, this short is reflected as an electrical short circuit to the wave-guide junction. Hence, it ensures low-resistance electrical continuity even though the mechanical connection between the two sections is not perfect. A choke joint is particularly useful as a rotating joint. (Secs. 2-1-2 and 2-1-3.)

8. Draw a simple cross-sectional diagram of a magnetron showing anode, cathode, and direction of electronic movement under the influence of a strong magnetic field.—See Fig. 4-4.

9. Briefly explain the principle of operation of the magnetron.—The magnetron tube consists of a cylindrical cathode surrounded by a multiresonant-cavity anode. The individual cavities are linked to the cathode-anode space by slots. A powerful magnet surrounds the anode structure.

Interaction between the magnetic field and the electrons traveling between cathode and anode causes the electrons to take an angular path toward the anode. Because of the differing velocities of the electron paths, the electrons bunch in an almost spoke-like manner. Each spoke, as it rotates across a cavity slot, delivers energy to the resonant cavity and initiates oscillation. In turn, the oscillations of each cavity influence the bunching of electrons, and oscillations are thereby sustained. Output is removed from the magnetron oscillator by inserting a probe into one of the cavities. (Sec. 2-2-1.)

10. Why is the anode in the magnetron in a radar transmitter normally maintained at ground potential?—It eliminates the problem of insulating the anode from the chassis, and at the

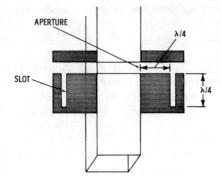

(A) Choke joint.

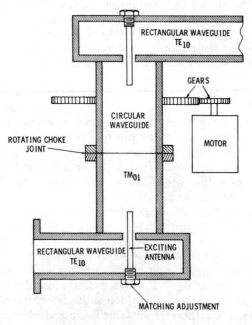

(B) Rotating choke joint.

Fig. 4-3. Choke joints.

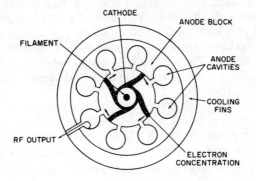

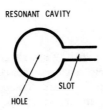
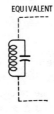

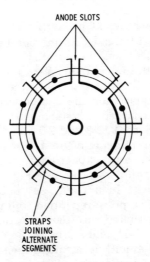

Fig. 4-4. Magnetron construction.

same time, it provides high-voltage protection. The anode-cathode voltage of a magnetron is very high. The high operating voltage can be obtained by pulsing the cathode at a high-negative potential instead of a high-positive potential on the anode. In so doing, the anode and case of the magnetron can be grounded (Fig. 2-18). Thus there need not be any high potential between the anode and ground which could present insulation problems and a possible shock hazard. (Sec. 2-2-1.)

11. What is the peak power of a radar pulse when the pulse width is 1 microsecond, pulse-repetition rate is 900, and the average power is 18 watts? What is the duty cycle?—Peak power is 20 kw; duty cycle, 0.0009, according to the following equations: (Sec. 1-8.)

$$\text{Peak Power} = \frac{\text{Average Power}}{\text{PRR} \times \text{Duration}} = \frac{18}{900 \times 1 \times 10^{-6}} = 20 \text{ kw}$$

$$\text{Duty Cycle} = \frac{\text{Average Power}}{\text{Peak Power}} = \frac{18}{20,000} = 0.0009$$

12. What is the purpose of the rotary spark gap used in some radar sets?—In older radar sets a rotary spark gap is used to discharge the pulse network into the load. When its rotating electrode passes a fixed electrode, an arc develops that discharges the line. The rotary gap represents a mechanical means of pulsing a magnetron instead of using an electronic switch, such as a thyratron.

13. What is the purpose of an artificial transmission line in a radar set?—The artificial transmission-line section serves as the pulse network and sets the duration and shape of the radar pulse. It does so with high stability because the pulse is dependent on the characteristics of the line rather than the associated circuit. The charge placed on the line between pulses by a high-voltage source is discharged as a stable pulse whenever the thyratron is triggered. (Secs. 1-11-2 and 2-3-5.)

14. Draw a simple diagram of an artificial transmission line showing inductance and capacitance, source of power, the load, and the electronic switch.—See Fig. 4-5.

15. What component in a radar set determines the pulse-repetition rate?—The pulse-repetition rate is determined by the master oscillator associated with the timer or synchronizer of the radar set. (Secs. 1-9, 1-11, and 2-3.)

16. What circuit element determines the operating frequency of the self-blocking oscillator?—The frequency of operation is determined largely by the grid-circuit time constant, namely the grid resistor and grid capacitor. Other factors, such as the trans-

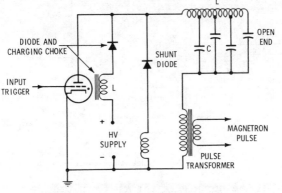

Fig. 4-5. Radar modulator.

former characteristics, also influence the repetition rate, but the rate is determined dominantly by the grid resistor and grid capacitor. (Sec. 2-3-3.)

4-3. RECEIVER-INDICATOR

1. Draw a simple block diagram of a radar receiver, labeling the signal crystal, local oscillator, AFC crystal stage, IF amplifier, and discriminator.—See Fig. 4-6.

2. Draw a simple frequency-converter circuit (mixer) as frequently used in radar superheterodyne receivers, and indicate which is the crystal stage.—See Fig. 4-7.

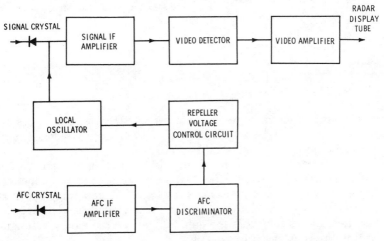

Fig. 4-6. Radar-receiver block diagram.

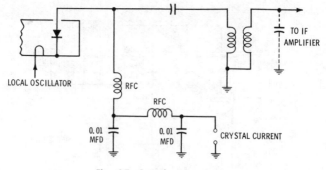

Fig. 4-7. Crystal mixer circuit.

3. What is the purpose of the klystron tube in a radar set?
—It serves as the local oscillator for the radar receiver. (Secs. 1-9 and 1-11.)

4. Briefly explain the principle of operation of the reflex klystron.—A typical klystron oscillator circuit is shown in Fig. 4-8. The tube consists of a cathode, focusing electrode, cavity resonator that serves as the anode, and repeller electrode. The electrons emitted from the cathode are focused into a fine beam that travels past the cavity-resonator gap to the repeller. The re-

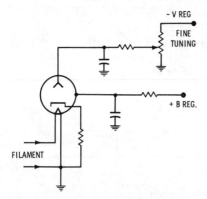

Fig. 4-8. Klystron-oscillator circuit.

peller has a negative potential that retards the electrons, causing them to return and pass nearby the cavity gap a second time, but traveling in the opposite direction.

The RF variation that builds up across the cavity gap varies the velocities of the electrons as they move toward the repeller. The electrons bunch together as they leave the gap (they are said to be velocity-modulated). The returned electrons arrive in bunches, and as they pass the gap, they excite the cavity resonant circuit, thus causing it to oscillate.

The strong oscillations in the cavity are removed via a probe and wave guide. They are applied to the mixer stage of the radar receiver. The oscillations in the resonant cavity also develop a changing voltage across the cavity gap. It is these variations that velocity-modulate, or bunch, the electrons arriving from the cathode. The feedback activity sustains the oscillations. (See Fig. 4-8, and Sec. 2-2-2.)

5. What nominal intermediate frequencies are commonly found in radar receivers?—Commonly they are 30 or 60 mc, although frequencies as low as 15 mc and as high as 120 mc are to be found.

6. What type of detector is frequently used in radar receivers?—The semiconductor diode is used most frequently.

7. What is the purpose of the discriminator stage in a radar superheterodyne?—The discriminator is a stage in the AFC system which applies a frequency-correcting voltage to the radar local oscillator so that incoming signals are converted to a precise IF frequency. This error voltage is used in correcting the frequency drift of magnetron or local oscillator. (Secs. 1-11 and 2-5-3.)

8. Briefly explain the purpose of the sensitivity of the time-control circuit in a radar set.—The sensitivity time-control circuit (STC) lowers the sensitivity of the receiver in receiving nearby target signals. As a result, the return from massive nearby objects and sea return will not be too brightly displayed on the radar screen. Nearby small objects will be displayed more distinctly, and the echoes from more distant targets will not be obscured by an overly bright central area. (Sec. 2-5-3.)

9. Draw a diagram of a cathode-ray tube as used in radar, showing the principal electrodes in the tube and the path of electron beam.—See Fig. 4-9.

10. Explain the principle of operation of the cathode-ray PPI tube, and explain the function of each electrode.—In the PPI tube (Fig. 4-9) an electron gun consisting of cathode, control grid, accelerating grid, and first anode, forms the electrons released from the heated cathode into a fine beam. The control grid regulates the intensity of the electron beam, while the difference of potential among the electrodes concentrates, or focuses, the beam. The beam is converged into a fine spot at the surface of the fluorescent screen. The electrons strike the screen with high impact, because of the high potential on the second anode and aquadag. The exact spot at which the beam strikes the screen depends on the position of the deflection coil and the current flow through it. The current in the deflection coil controls the radial motion of the beam from the center of the PPI screen out to the periphery. This radial motion corresponds to a time base that matches the particular range setting of the radar set.

The rotational position of the trace line is determined by the actual physical rotation of the deflection coil. This deflection-coil rotation is synchronized to the antenna rotation. Thus the radar display is calibrated in range as a function of the target distance from the center, and in bearing as a function of the angular position of the trace line when scanning over the target. (Secs. 1-10-2, 1-11-3, 2-2-4, and 2-4-7.)

11. **What is the purpose of aquadag coating for cathode-ray tubes?**—The coating acts as a part of the second anode to give the final acceleration to the CRT beam electrons. It provides a

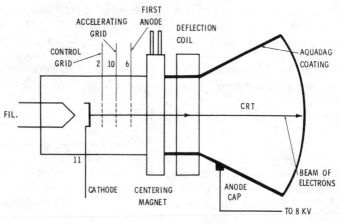

Fig. 4-9. PPI radar tube.

conductive coating that also shields the electron-beam deflection from the influence of strong external fields.

12. **Draw a simple diagram showing how a synchro generator located in the radar-antenna assembly is connected to a synchro motor, located at the indicator, which rotates the deflection coil. Show proper designation of all leads, designating where AC voltages (if needed) are applied.** (See Fig. 4-10. Sec. 2-4-4.)

13. **What is meant by bearing resolution of a radar set?**— Bearing resolution is a measure of the capability of a radar set to delineate between two closely spaced targets at the same range. (Secs. 1-6 and 2-1-3.)

14. **Explain how heading flash and range-marking circles are produced on a radar PPI scope.**—A bright heading flash is reproduced on the radar screen whenever the radar antenna

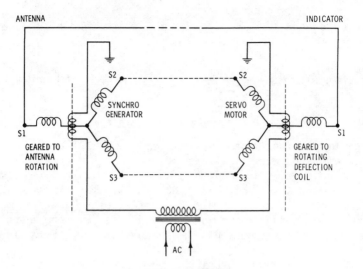

ANTENNA   INDICATOR

S2   S2

SYNCHRO   SERVO
GENERATOR   MOTOR

S1   S1

GEARED TO   GEARED TO
ANTENNA   ROTATING
ROTATION   DEFLECTION
                                                                              COIL

S3   S3

AC

Fig. 4-10. Synchro system.

directs its beam dead ahead. Dead ahead refers to the forward
direction of travel of the boat or aircraft. Usually a switching
arrangement is used in which the switch closes whenever the
antenna points dead ahead. In so doing, a so-called intensifier
pulse is generated and applied to the grid-cathode circuit of the
PPI tube. It causes an increase in beam current, and a bright
marking appears on the screen of the radar display tube. (See
Secs. 3-1-2 and 3-2-2.)

Range-mark signals are also applied to the grid-cathode circuit
of the PPI tube, causing an increase in illumination whenever
the range-mark signals arrive. These range-mark signals are generated within the radar set and correspond in their spacing to a
specific radar-range travel time. Thus their position on the display
tube corresponds to a specific mileage. Although the range-mark
signals are in themselves very short duration pulses, or "pips,"
they blend together with trace line rotation to form complete
circles on the PPI display. These circles are called range rings.

In the range-mark generator a series of sine waves is formed
under control of a timing-gate pulse. These sine waves are
squared and differentiated, forming very sharp signal spikes. The
separation between spikes corresponds to a specific calibration
time (1-mile excursion time, 5-mile excursion time, etc.). (Secs.
1-10-2, 1-11, 2-4-5 and 2-4-7.)

**15. What is the distance in nautical miles to a target if it
takes 123 microseconds for a radar pulse to travel from a
radar antenna to the target, back to the antenna and be dis-**

played on the PPI scope?—Range is approximately 10 miles. (Secs. 1-1, 2-4-1, 2-4-2, and 2-4-7.)

$$\text{Range (miles)} = \frac{\text{Total Time in } \mu \text{ Secs}}{\text{Velocity in } \mu \text{ Secs/Mile}} = \frac{123}{12.3} = 10 \text{ miles}$$

4-4. RADAR MAINTENANCE

In studying the maintenance questions use Secs. 3-1-3 and 3-2-3 as reference material.

1. What is sea return on a radar scope?—Radar waves that are reflected from bodies of water. Such reflections from the waves of the sea are referred to as sea return. These cause a bright illumination in the central area of the PPI radar display. Radar circuits that minimize the so-called sea clutter are often included.

2. What may cause bright flashing pie-shaped sections to appear on a radar PPI scope?—Flashing pie-shaped sections, or "spoking," can be caused by a variety of defects. It is a cyclic-type of defect that can be caused by a defect in some synchronized activity in the radar set. For example, a defective AFC crystal could permit a receiver drift that would cause the receiver sensitivity to vary at a cyclic rate. Other duplexer and transmitter defects can cause a similar disturbance. Servo defects and loss of synchronism between antenna rotation and trace-line rotation may cause a similar defect.

3. What precaution should a radar serviceman observe to prevent personal injury to himself or other persons when making repairs or adjustments to a radar set?—Radar sets operate at high power and with high voltage. High voltages are always a hazard; power should be shut off and high-voltage capacitors should be discharged with a grounding stick before you work on the "innards" of a set. If power-on work must be done, it should be performed carefully and with someone nearby who can turn off the equipment quickly if need be. Be careful not to draw arcs when making on-site checks in the presence of gasoline or battery fumes. Employ the usual precautions in handling the special radar tubes. A radar display tube, like any CRT type, is subject to implosion.

4. Is there any danger in testing or operating radar equipment aboard ship when explosives or inflammable cargo is being handled?—Yes, because radar sets employ high voltages which have a tendency to arc. Furthermore, the concentrated power in a microwave signal from a high-powered radar set is capable of overheating certain flammable materials.

5. **What is the purpose of an echo box in a radar system? Explain the principle of operation of an echo box. What indications may be expected on a radar scope when an echo box is used and the radar set is operating properly? when the radar set is not operating properly?**—An echo box serves as an artificial target which can be used to check radar transmitter and receiver performance. The echo box consists of a resonant cavity which is shock-excited into oscillation by some of the transmit pulse energy. This energy is reradiated by the echo box. In fact, even after the conclusion of the transmit pulse the echo box continues to reradiate until all of the energy that has been supplied to it has been dissipated. This reradiated energy is picked up by the receiver and displayed on the PPI screen. Thus the echo box is acting as an artificial target.

The length and shape of the spoke pattern displayed becomes an indicator of radar-system performance. A decrease in the spoke length or any other distortion of its shape as compared to past results indicates improper operation.

6. **What effect, if any, does the accumulation of soot or dirt on the antenna reflector have on the operation of a ship radar?**—A thin accumulation has very little influence; excessive amounts may cause some deterioration of performance. The higher the frequency of operation and the sharper the desired beam, the more adverse will be the influence of an excessive accumulation. Most modern radars include a plastic radome which protects the installation from dirt and weather, thus extending the life of moving parts and providing more effective isolation of the antenna and wave guide from the ill effects of moisture, etc.

7. **In a radar set what are the indications of (A) a defective magnetron, (B) a weak magnet in the magnetron?**—A defective magnetron is indicated by an improper magnetron current or absent, weak, or fuzzy target presentations on the screen. Noise and range marks will appear normal. Protective relays may drop out, and there may be some modulator arcing.

A weak magnet causes an increase in magnetron current. There may be a low output, a change in frequency, or a change in the spectrum distribution of the transmitted pulse.

8. **What symptoms on a radar scope would indicate that the radar-receiver mixer crystal is defective?**—Target signals would be absent, weak, or fuzzy. The noise level would be higher. An echo box test would show a decline in receiver sensitivity.

9. **What care should be taken when handling silicon crystal-rectifier cartridges for replacement in radar superheterodyne receivers?**—The radar-receiver crystals are sensitive to very

weak signals and can be damaged by the application of above-rating voltages, whether from a static charge or by an excessive test-meter voltage or current.

10. What precautions should a radar serviceman take when working with or handling a magnetron?—The magnetron should not be jarred or struck sharply, and it should be handled with the same care with which you would service any delicate electronic component. The magnet should not be overheated or struck sharply.

11. What precautions should the service and maintenance operator observe when replacing the cathode-ray tube in a radar set?—Power should be off and high-voltage capacitor charges drained off. A wise precaution is the use of gloves and goggles. As in the handling of any cathode-ray tube, the strain should be placed on the screen end rather than the neck of the tube.

12. Name at least four pieces of radio or electronic equipment aboard ship which might suffer interference from radar equipment.—Communications receivers, radiotelephone and radiotelegraph equipment, DF (direction finder), long-range navigation equipment (LORAN), and intercommunication facilities.

13. Why is it important that all units of a radar installation be thoroughly bonded to the ship's electrical ground?—Radar sets operate at high power, and furthermore, they generate high-powered short-duration pulses. The magnitude and number of harmonic pulse components are great. Consequently, the set must be well grounded to minimize the radiation or transmission along the power lines of these components. Proper grounding of high-powered equipment is also necessary in the reduction of shock hazard and other annoying voltage build-ups.

14. Describe how various types of interference from a radar installation may be apparent to a person when listening to a radiocommunications receiver.—Several types of interference can originate at a radar set. Because so many harmonics are generated, it is possible to hear heterodynes, or "birdies," at various points as you tune over the frequency spectrum of the communications receiver. Often these heterodynes are spaced at regular intervals over a given frequency spectrum because of their harmonic relation. Tone or a steady hash can be picked up because the pulse-repetition rate itself is in the audible range. Other sources of noise are motors, generators, and power-circuit components.

15. Briefly explain why radar interference to a radiotelephone receiver is often characterized by a steady tone in the radio speaker.—The pulses generated in a radar set are in the audible frequency range. Therefore, in cases of interference it is the modulation which occurs at the pulse repetition rate that is heard.

16. At what frequencies should the radar serviceman look for radar interference on ships equipped with radar?—The harmonic content of the high-powered short-duration pulses is such that interference components can be spread over a considerable frequency spectrum. However, of primary importance are those frequencies used by the particular shipboard station. Thus, it is wise to tune over each of the frequency bands assigned to the marine service. Direction finding and radiotelegraph assignments are made at various segments of the spectrum between 100 kc and 515 kc. LORAN and marine radiotelephone assignments are in the frequency spectrum between 1.8 mc and 3 mc. Long-distance marine communications are assigned spot-frequency bands between 3 and 30 mc. There are also VHF band harbor radio assignments.

17. Is there any likelihood of a radar installation causing interference to radio receivers if long connecting lines are used between the radar transmitter and the radar modulator?—Yes, particularly if the lines are not shielded or properly terminated. The modulator pulse is of high magnitude and is rich in harmonics; it can be a definite source of interference. In fact, it is preferable to use as short a length of line as possible between the modulator and transmitter.

18. How are the various types of radar interference recognized in (A) auto-alarm equipment, (B) direction-finding equipment?—Listening checks are made. Heterodynes and audible tones are likely to be heard when interference is present. Auto-alarm sets include a monitor jack into which you can insert a headset for listening purposes.

19. In checking a direction finder for interference caused by radar equipment, would it be a good policy to check for interference while the DF loop is being rotated?—This might be a good method to isolate the source of interference. You can determine whether the interference is coming from the radar set of a nearby boat or the radar set under test. It might also help in determining whether the interference is being coupled over the common power circuits of the boat or by direct radiation from modulator-transmitter.

20. What steps might be taken by a radar serviceman to eliminate a steady-tone type of interference to radiocommunication receivers or interference to LORAN receivers evidenced by spikes?—Of principal concern is shielding and proper termination of pulse lines. Both the receiving equipment of concern and the radar equipment should be grounded and bonded. Power circuits at both systems should include RF filters because of the high-frequency distribution of the pulse harmonics. A final step may be to try additional physical separation between systems.

21. What steps might be taken by a radar serviceman to reduce grass on a LORAN scope or motor-generator noise in a communications receiver?—Shielding, bounding of units together, and grounding are of principal concern. Motors and generators should be filtered where possible and appropriate filters should be installed in the power line. All types of sparking interference should be eliminated, and commutators and brushes must be kept in good condition.

22. List at least two types of indications on a LORAN scope that signify that a radar installation is causing interference to the LORAN.—There is a high noise level as made apparent by grass near the sweep line. Strong pulse components from the radar will cause spokes to move right or left across the LORAN display tube.

23. What considerations should be taken into account when selecting the location of the radar-antenna assembly aboard ship?—The antenna should be mounted in the clear and spaced as far as is practical from obstacles that may influence antenna pattern or produce obscuring patterns on the radar screen. In some installations obstructions are unavoidable, and if obstructions are present, the antenna should be mounted so that these obstructions are to the rear of the antenna.

To minimize attenuation the wave-guide span should be kept as short as is practical. The radar-antenna system must be well supported physically so that it can readily withstand environmental extremes.

24. When installing wave guides, why should long, perfectly level sections of wave guide be avoided? Why is a small hole about 1/8 inch in diameter drilled on the underside of an elbow in a wave guide near the point where it enters the radar transmitter?—Moisture content in the line must be kept at a minimum to prevent discontinuities and resultant attenuation. Moisture must be kept from the duplexer and transmitter-receiver to prevent poor performance and possible equipment damage. Thus, a drain hole or absorbent material is inserted near the entrance point. Long, perfectly level runs are to be avoided, because they are especially prone to an accumulation of moisture that does not drain off quickly.

25. To prevent moisture from entering the wave guide, what precautions should be taken when installing vertical sections

of wave guide with choke-coupling flanges?—A good vertical mounting should be made so as to minimize the collection of moisture. Gaskets can be used to ensure a more weather-proof joint.

Appendix

PART 83 RULES AND REGULATIONS FOR SHIPBOARD RADAR

83.155 Waivers of Operator License.

(b) *For ship radar.* (1) No radio operator license is required for the operation on board ship, during the course of the normal rendition of service, of ship radar stations: *Provided,* That the following conditions are met or provided for by the licensee of the station:

(i) The radar equipment shall employ as its frequency determining element a non-tunable, pulse-type magnetron;

(ii) The radar equipment shall be capable of being operated during the course of normal rendition of service in accordance with the radio law and the rules and regulations of the Commission by means of exclusively external controls, and

(iii) Operation during the course of normal rendition of service pursuant to this subparagraph (1) must be performed exclusively by the master of the radar-equipped ship or by one or more other persons responsible to him and authorized by him to do so.

(2) All adjustments or tests during or coincident with the installation, servicing, or maintenance of the equipment while it is radiating energy must be performed by or under the immediate supervision and responsibility of a person holding a first or second class commercial radio operator license, radiotelephone or radiotelegraph, containing a ship-radar endorsement, who shall be responsible for the proper functioning of the equipment in accordance with the radio law and the Commission's rules and regulations and for the avoidance and prevention of harmful interference from improper transmitter external effects: *Provided, however,* That nothing in this subparagraph shall be construed to prevent persons not holding such licenses or not holding such licenses so endorsed from making replacements of fuses or of receiving-type tubes.

(3) Nothing in this subparagraph shall be construed to change or diminish in any respect the responsibility of any ship radar station licensee for having and maintaining control over the station licensed to him, or for the proper functioning and operation of such station in accordance with the terms of the station license.

(c) *For survival craft.* No radio operator license is required for the operation of a survival craft station while it is being used solely for survival purposes. [*83.155 (b) (1) as amended; par. (c) as adopted eff. 10-1-62; IV (62)-1*]

83.156 Posting of Operator License.

When a licensed operator is required for the operation of a station subject to this part, the original license of each such operator while he is employed or designated as radio operator of the station shall be posted in a conspicuous place at the principal location on board ship at which the station is operated: *Provided*, That in the case of stations of a portable nature, including marine-utility stations, or in the case where the operator holds a restricted radiotelephone operator permit, the operator may in lieu of posting have on his person either his required operator license or a duly issued verification card (FCC Form 758-F) attesting to the existence of that license.

83.157 Adjustment or Test of Equipment.

Notwithstanding any other provisions of this subpart (except 83.155(b)(2) which specifically covers ship radar stations), all adjustments or tests of radio transmitting apparatus in any station subject to this part during or coincident with the installation, servicing, or maintenance of such apparatus which may affect the proper operation of such station, must be performed by or under the immediate supervision and responsibility of a person holding a first or second class commercial radio operator license, either radiotelephone or radiotelegraph as may be appropriate for the class of station involved, who shall be responsible for the proper functioning of the station equiment.

Subpart P—Use of Radiodetermination
[Subpart P title as amended eff. 10-1-62; IV (62)-1]

83.401 Assignable Frequencies for Direction Finding.

(a) The frequency 410 kc/s is the assigned frequency for direction-finding.

(b) As an exception, on condition that signals of distress, urgency and safety, and calls and answers, are not interfered with, the calling channel of which 500 kc/s is the assigned frequency may be used additionally and with discretion, by ship stations for direction-finding; exclusively in Regions 1 and 3 outside areas of heavy radio traffic.

(c) In the event of distress, the following frequencies may be used for radio direction finding for purposes of search and rescue by any licensed ship or survival craft station:

410 kc/s   500 kc/s   2182 kc/s   8364 kc/s

[83.401 (c) as amended eff. 10-1-62; IV (62)-1]

83.402 [Reserved]

[83.402 deleted eff. 10-1-62; IV (62)-1]

83.403 Radiodetermination by Cable-Repair Ship.

Provided radio transmitting equipment attached to a cable-marker buoy has been adequately described in an application for ship radio station license for a cable repair ship with which the buoy is associated, and provided further that such equipment is authorized in the related ship station license, that equipment may be operated (outside the territorial waters of a foreign country) on such radio channels within the band 285-325 kc/s (285-315 kc/s only in Region 1) as may be expressly authorized in each case by the Commission under authority of the ship station license, with A1 or A2 emission and a maximum plate input power of 30 watts: *Provided*, That interference shall not be caused by such operation to any maritime radionavigation service. The call signals that must be used for a transmitter operating under the provisions of this section shall be the regularly assigned call of the ship station with which the buoy is associated, to be followed by the letters "BT," and the identifying number of the buoy. The buoy transmitter shall be continuously monitored by a licensed radiotelegraph operator on board the associated cable-repair ship. Should a frequency deviation in excess of the authorized frequency tolerance, or interference to the service of any other station, be reported or observed, the radiation of the transmitter shall be suspended until the excessive deviation is eliminated or until the transmitter can be operated without causing interference.

[*83.403 as amended eff. 10-1-62; IV (62)-1*]

83.404   Assignable Frequencies above 2400 Mc/s.

(a) The following frequency bands, when designated in the station license, are authorized for use by ship radionavigation stations (including ship radar stations):

> 2900 to 3100 Mc/s
> 5460 to 5650 Mc/s
> 9300 to 9500 Mc/s

The use of the band 5460 to 5650 Mc/s is limited to shipborne radar. Transmitters in ship radionavigation stations (including developmental stations) which are authorized for operation in the 3000 to 3246 Mc/s band as of April 16, 1958, and which operate on frequencies between 3100 and 3246 Mc/s may continue to be authorized for operation on the same vessel provided that any renewal of the authorization shall be subject to the condition that no protection shall be given from any interference caused by emission from United States Government stations operating in the 3100 to 3246 Mc/s band.

(b) The following frequency bands, when designated in the station license, are authorized for use by ship radiolocation stations:

(1) 2450 to 2500 Mc/s, on condition that harmful interference shall not be caused to the fixed and mobile services, and on the condition that no protection shall be given from interference caused by emission from industrial, scientific, or medical equipment;

(2)

> 2900 to 3100 Mc/s
> 5460 to 5650 Mc/s
> 9300 to 9500 Mc/s

The use of frequencies within these bands for radiolocation shall not cause harmful interference to the radionavigation service and to the Government radiolocation service. Each ship radiolocation station authorized to operate in the band 3000 to 3246 Mc/s as of April 16, 1958, and which operates on frequencies between 3100 and 3246 Mc/s may continue to operate in the band 3100 to 3246 Mc/s for the duration of the term of its authorization in effect as of that date. Renewals of such authorizations, however, shall be contingent upon the condition that each such station shall not cause harmful interference to United States Government services.

[*83.404 as amended eff. 10-1-62; IV (62)-1*]

83.405   Special Provisions Applicable to Ship-Radar Stations

(a) A ship-radar station may be operated under an interim ship station license. The use and operation of a radar station on board ship under the authority conferred by an interim ship station license shall be subject to and in accordance with all applicable rules of the Commission.

(b) Each ship-radar station installation the manufacture of which was completed on or after 1947 shall be furnished with a durable name plate with the manufacturer's name, transmitter model number, and month and year of completion of manufacture permanently inscribed thereon. Such name plate shall be affixed to the indicator housing at the principal radar operating position or to some other component of the radar installation which is readily accessible for inspection.

(c) Each ship-radar station license issued shall be subject to the condition that the station licensee, in relation to the proper operation of the station in accordance with the radio law, and rules and regulations of the Commission, will be represented on board the radar-equipped vessel by the person who at any given time occupies the position of master.

(d) The following provisions shall apply to ship-radar stations:

(1) The station licensee of each ship-radar station shall provide and require to be kept at the station a permanent installation and maintenance record. Entries in this record shall be made by or under the personal direction of the responsible installation, service, or maintenance operator concerned in each particular instance, but the station licensee shall have joint responsibility with the responsible operator concerned for the faithful and accurate making of such entries as are required by the paragraph.

(2) Each entry in this record shall be personally signed by the responsible operator concerned.

(3) The following entries shall be made in this record:

(i) The date and place of initial installation.

(ii) Any necessary steps taken to remedy any interference found to exist at the time of such installation.

(iii) The nature of any complaint (including interference to radio communication) arising subsequent to initial installation, and the date thereof.

(iv) The reason for the trouble leading to the complaint, including the name of any component or component part which failed or was misadjusted.

(v) Remedial measures taken, and date thereof.

(vi) The name, license number, and date of the ship-radar operator endorsement on the first or second class radio operator license of the responsible operator performing or immediately supervising the installation, servicing, or maintenance.

(e) Until the Commission shall otherwise provide, the ship-radar station licensee, by such arrangement as may be necessary with the ship master, operating agency, or ship owner, shall, upon specific request made by the Commission, be responsible for the submission of such reports as are requested by the Commission to show the value and practical performance of the ship-radar station. For assistance in preparing these reports, daily records, when the radar installation is tested or used, should, when practicable, be kept showing at least the following:

(1) Approximate number of hours of use while the ship is in operation;

(2) Number of service failures, and duration, nature, and cause of each failure if known;

(3) Performance under local weather conditions which are unfavorable for marine navigation; and

(4) Unusual incidents, including, among others, cases in which radar may have aided or hindered safe operation of the ship.

(f) In addition to the installation and maintenance record required by paragraphs (d) and (e) of this section, the following documents shall be available for reference on board each radar-equipped vessel whose ship-radar station is licensed by the Commission:

(1) Part 8 of this chapter.

(2) At least one set of instructions from the respective manufacturer relative to the use and operation of the particular type of ship-radar installation.

(g) No provisions of this part shall require any ship-radar station to transmit any signal (s) intended solely for the purpose of identifying that station.

Index